THE WAY THE DAY BREAKS

THE WAY THE DAY BREAKS

David Roberts

WEATHERGLASS BOOKS

I.M.

Harry McKell
(24th March 1924 – 17th August 2005)

PART ONE

1

but we're not going to be, are we though.

Why ever not is the thing isn't it really, what's stopping us. Think of the benefits think big, think. Think about it, the tax breaks and, well, there must be more to it than that. I can't believe I've been wasting, not wasting my time so much as, can't believe I've only just thought this one, started thinking this one through.

Stop it Sinclair, please really, it's beginning to hurt.

I once laughed so much I was nearly sick and it never did me any harm.

Not when you were driving you didn't. Concentrate really, you need to concentrate on the road.

But what's stopping us seriously I mean, what's holding us back. I'm not messing around here, honestly. What would it take as a family for us to become a religion, get the tax breaks and have pilgrims offering us gifts or respects or what have you, hard currency.

Sinclair please, stop it.

Not now this one, this one's a winner love. I mean think about it think. We could do baptisms in the pond, 'cept we couldn't go calling them baptisms, would have to think of a different name for it, our water ceremony.

But we don't have a pond dad.

Good point in the back, well made. First thing when we get home we're digging. You hear that Christopher? Me and you digging when we get back.

Isn't it going to be dark when we get back dad?

First thing in the morning then, first thing in the morning we'll be beginning our ceremonial pond, father and son digging together. Any luck the services'll be getting started by the end of next month, half term say. Maybe we'll need a placard or something, some kind of notice. What you think Helen, you think you could think up a placard for the front verge, the rose bed.

But I thought we were atheists dad, that's what you always say to grandma.

Not when we can be a religion we're not but, thinking about it it shouldn't have to be, there's nothing stopping, not as if the two have to cancel each other out is it though?

Sinclair this is getting a bit.

What love I mean, honestly, all I'm saying is you can be an atheist and a religion at the same time is all I'm saying, why not I mean, why should it matter what you don't believe as to tax breaks and other people, whether we get other people believing in us, donating to the cause.

This is all a bit moot Sinclair.

Be that as it may I mean really, all this debate's holding us back and, any more excuses in the back? Thought not. Tomorrow is pond day then. Any luck and we'll have an altar up by the time you're back at school.

That's next week dad.

I know full well it's next week, we'll just have to work hard is all. All of us will have to pull our socks up on this one. Seriously, I'm not having any shirking.

Will we be back in time for *Neighbours* dad?

I haven't taken you lot on holiday, haven't driven to the Pyrenees and back so as we can get home in time for bleeding *Neighbours*.

Dad swore again.

No he didn't. It was a qualifier.

Why isn't it a qualifier when I bloodywell say it then.

Language Christopher. Really, do you want your brother hearing that. Set an example, please.

But dad said, why is it ok for dad to say it and not me?

Because your father, me and your father have paid for this holiday and.

But he.

But nothing Helen really, show a little respect for a change.

But I didn't.

You didn't have to, I don't know, it's written all over your face sometimes but, what's that smell?

It's probably the cheese.

No, it's not the, no the cheese isn't even that strong.

It is in the back.

It pongs.

It reeks.

Stinky mouldy cheese.

Mouldy stinky cheese.

3

Stinkorama.

Stinky bloody cheese.

Michael! I will not have you using words like that really, look what you've done Christopher setting a bad example and, don't you say a word Helen, I've got my eye on you.

But I didn't do anything.

I've got my eye on you is all I'm saying and, stop distracting things. That smell, it's not the engine is it Sinclair?

I'm supposing you'd need some form of belief system, some code of ethics or dietary restrictions at the very least.

Sinclair?

If you were going to, if we're to go about becoming a religion then we need to think about this stuff, get a few things straight.

Have you even heard a word I've been saying Sinclair?

Yes dear I, run it by me again.

The bleeding smell Sinclair. I don't know why I even bother sometimes.

What smell love, what is it you can smell?

The engine Sinclair, honestly. How can you not it's, the engine's overheating again.

I can't smell anything.

You never can with all your cigarettes can you though, seriously Sinclair, what did I even marry, you're going to have to pull over.

I can't just pull over here love.

I wasn't saying you should pull over here just, that it might be an idea to, look. There's parking in three miles.

4

If you think we'll make it.

We're not going to break down are we?

Not again dad, please can we not break down again?

Look, no one said anything about, no one's, we're not going to break down, I'm just going to pull over in, oh, I'd say about one and a half, let's hope they're not country miles from now and we'll get a chance to stretch our legs a bit, maybe have a quick brew or game of French cricket say.

French cricket?

As long as you can play away from the road.

Frenchy.

Frenchy, Frenchy.

Frenchee.

That's enough now, just make sure, you can only play if it's well away from the road and, I can't promise there'll be space for it.

Frencheee.

Yes Michael, French cricket.

Who'd of thought, back in England and playing French cricket already.

But we always play French cricket dad.

Look there's no promises, we can't be promising until we've seen how it is. You listening?

Are we nearly there?

It won't be long now Michael just, what's this sign saying.

Five hundred yards.

I've seen it love.

I'm only making sure.

That you are.

Then why say that.

Look, I think we all need a little fresh air is what we need. Besides which it'll give us the chance to think, make a plan even.

About what?

Us. Becoming a religion.

Will you give it a rest Sinclair really, pull over.

Don't worry.

I'm only pointing it out.

I know you are love.

Well why did you?

Because I'm letting you know I've seen it and, we're here now aren't we. Wait till I've stopped the engine.

Where's the tennis racket?

Not while the engine's running Christopher.

In the boot. No wait, you'll damage the cheese I'll get it just, wait, right.

You've heard your father.

Yes mum.

Here we are then.

Frenchy.

Over there, play over there and no big hits Christopher please.

I won't mum.

There's a good boy. You think it's anything Sinclair, anything up with the engine I mean.

Just, I'd have thought it's just a little overhot is all but, best that we leave, let it cool a little before having a look.

I'll get us a brew on.

Thanks love.

It'll have to be powdered milk I'm afraid.

I thought there was some left, in the cool box.

We threw it, remember? In the car park before the ferry.

That we did. Thanks love.

Be nice won't it, to be drinking English milk again.

That it will and, would you look at that.

Isn't it just.

The three of them, playing together.

Isn't it.

It certainly is.

Christopher! I thought I said no big hits.

Sorry mum.

You will be when the game gets stopped. How's it looking Sinclair?

It's nothing so much, I think just, like we said a little overhot and the radiator could do, a bit of a top-up of the radiator should be doing it.

It's not leaking is it?

I shouldn't have thought so, should have thought it's just the heat of it but, I'll have a proper look, open her up when we're home and, deary me, it's glugged that easy enough.

Are we going to be alright?

Well it's not quite the full shilling but, to get us home I mean, I'd like to say yes but it seems, seems to be going through it rather quick and, was that the last of it?

The water yes.

That'll be that then.

You think it'll, we are going to make it aren't we?

In all probability, if I was a betting man I'd be saying yes, be taking these odds but, it's the consequences if it goes wrong I suppose, if it were to bleed dry that'd be.

Would it be the engine gone Sinclair?

I wouldn't know about that wouldn't say it'd be gone gone, but. You'd think it'd be salvageable just, it'd be a hell of a task, lot of work even getting it, how we'd go about getting ourselves home again.

Is it, you think it's worth the risk of it?

Well look at our options, I don't know, don't know if I fancy pitching tents here I mean look at this gravel it wouldn't be a comfy night would it, it'd be an issue even getting the pegs in and probably, chances are we'd make it.

But if we don't.

If we don't.

If we don't we.

Well, we wouldn't, would we?

How about, you think this could do it Sinclair?

The wine?

Well just this, would this vrac be enough I mean it's only cooking, have you smelt it, I'm not sure it's even good for cooking it's turned, near enough gone and turned to cleaning wine.

Just, let me have a taste it's, oh, I see what you mean it's, how much did we pay for this again love?

I'd have to check the receipt Sinclair but I shouldn't have thought it'd, couldn't have been more than forty francs say.

Not to worry love it's, whatever it was, if it was twice three times that it'd be cheap, even gone to vinegar it'd be, imagine.

You think it'll work?

Think it'll work? The water and the wine why not, the engine. The engine'll need a fettle but, the engine was going to need a fettle anyway wasn't it and wine in the radiator, not water but water and wine together this is beautiful this is, the beauty of it hot, oh, this brew's gone down a treat.

You finished with your cup?

Thanks love it, that hit the spot thanks.

Best that we be getting it over with I suppose.

Just, let me smoke this.

I'm not rushing you.

I know you're not love. Kids! Be finishing up will you. Good catch Michael.

Well done. Last ball Helen.

Game over folks. Well that was a bit of fun, wasn't it? Always good to stretch your legs isn't it, makes the journey smoother I mean.

Will we make it dad?

We're not going to get stranded again are we?

Not after the minor little, what me and your mother just witnessed we won't.

Will it happen again?

Look, we never did get stranded and no, it won't happen again, alright? Now me and your mother were just talking things through while you lot were off gallivanting with your French cricket and we think it's really important that we get this one right, get off on a good foot with it. In this case half measures won't really do because, well, you'd be in danger of becoming a cult then wouldn't you, only achieving cult status? So yes, we're going to need well-defined roles if we're going to have this up and running by the time school starts back. Christopher, you're with me on the pond, that right, and Helen's already volunteered to work on the placard so that leaves you with something to do, doesn't it Michael? What you think? Because definitely, you've definitely got a big part to play in all this. Maybe we could have you working on doctrine, although I suppose that essentially that's just us, isn't it? Essentially we are the doctrine.

Is someone ill?

Why, what do you mean is someone ill?

What's doctoring?

Not doctoring no, doctrine sorry, are you having trouble hearing in the back? Doctrine. It's part of what it's going to mean, for us to become a religion.

Why are we even, why are you still talking about this dad?

Tax purposes but not just tax purposes no, it would be about us wouldn't it, the five of us together getting some enjoyment out of life. That's it I mean. Because if it were just tax purposes receiving donations having pilgrims visit then what is that, what is that really? Why not allow ourselves to dream a little, enjoy it I mean. I mean look at Jesus.

Not Jesus Sinclair, really not this again.

All I'm saying is look at the man. All that, spreading bread and fishes, possessing pigs and Methuselah.

Methuselah's Old Testament Sinclair.

Well not Methuselah then but, look at him, putting in all that effort and what did he have to show for it? Not one drop one penny, nothing. It wasn't till years, a century or something later, that things got going was it. And where was he then, when the going got good? But, us. This life is all. All I'm saying is I'd like us to be seeing the benefits sooner rather than later is all I'm trying to say.

Sinclair.

Yes love.

The road Sinclair.

I am looking love.

Well maybe you could drive like you're looking, really Sinclair slow down.

I'm being careful love don't worry yourself, honestly. Have a little faith.

Will we still go camping when we're a religion dad?

Good question Helen. Will we still go camping when we're a religion, I like that. When we're a religion, good. It's positive, yes and, I don't see why not. I shouldn't have thought anything should stop us from camping in the future. Old age apart, not even that even. What do you think love, can you see any good reason for us to stop going camping. Look there, a kestrel.

A kestrel, look.

A kestrel. Did you see it, did you see the kestrel Michael, Christopher?

Yes dad, we've seen loads of kestrels already today dad.

Still, it's always nice though isn't it, seeing a kestrel.

The kestrel is the only British bird that can actually hover.

Good Michael, good.

He's only sucking up, being a swot again.

I am not a swot.

Don't listen to him Michael, being a swot is a, there's nothing wrong with being a swot.

I am not a swot.

Swot.

Enough of that Helen really, you two, will you leave your little brother alone. He's only seven.

I'm nearly eight.

Don't listen to them Michael, we'll be needing you to do some swotting if we're ever to get this doctrine sorted out. Anyway, look who's talking in the back. I thought you said you were looking forward to school Helen?

I never said that, honestly. I'm looking forward to seeing my friends not going back to school.

How was Lisa when you spoke to her?

She's good, yeah.

And what's she been doing with her holidays?

She's been watching *Neighbours*.

Really Helen, you wouldn't rather of been, how is Ramsay Street I mean, what's been happening down under?

Scott and Charlene got married.

They had the wedding?

I can't believe we missed it.

Well, if you'd rather have been watching *Neighbours*.

Scott and Charlene got married dad.

So I've heard, but, that is big news isn't it. What are you going to do love, however will you cope?

Lisa videoed it.

She did, crikey. Really, Lisa videoed *Neighbours*.

I'm going to go round, watch it tomorrow.

Videoing *Neighbours* that's well, good foresight I suppose. Good for you love, still getting to watch your programme.

What do you know dad seriously, Scott and Charlene.

Well, I'm glad it's worked out for them. Always good isn't it, when love stays the course.

Sinclair really, how can you be, just because they've got married doesn't mean love's stayed the course.

I know it doesn't but, it's a start at least.

What's it matter though, how it starts when it's a soap? When all they do in soaps is have affairs and there's more divorces, more splitting up than real life even? So far as I can tell getting married's not the start of it hardly.

Can't fault you so much there love. Hear that Helen, you hear your mother then? Don't put too much stock in this one, we don't want you getting upset if things don't work out for them, ok?

Work out for who dad?

Scott and Charlene.

But they're only on *Neighbours* dad, *Neighbours* isn't, it's just the telly you know.

Good well, I'm glad you're aware of that and, aren't you the one who's been saying she'd rather have been watching, aren't

13

you the one who's going round Lisa's first thing tomorrow so as to catch it up?

Not first thing dad I'm not, Lisa's at her grandma's, won't be back till the afternoon probably. She's going to ring.

Gives you a chance to help with the unpacking doesn't it.

Are we not unpacking when we get back?

I shouldn't have thought so, not if we can help it anyway. Save for the essentials things'll be alright for a night in the car and, oh, will you look at that, really, isn't that a thing to be coming home to?

Are we nearly?

Yes Michael, not long now you can see the, look you can see the pinnacle already, it's just about catching the light still. How come you're turning off here?

So as to get a break from this traffic. That and the view, I like the view better this way, for a change sometimes anyhow.

But isn't it?

Not by much, five minutes maybe and well, would you look at that. What do you think, in the back there? Was it worth it, in the end? You think you'll want to do it all again next year?

Never.

I don't ever want to, don't want to ever be forced to set foot in this car again.

Not the car no. Call this gratitude, my own skin indeed. Not the car, the holiday. You think you'll be ready for another holiday next year, won't be too grown-up for camping by then?

Suppose so.

14

Hear that love? They suppose so well, I suppose we must be doing something about right, mustn't we just. And the journey wasn't too, you got your French cricket didn't you, not every day that you get to play French cricket on a car journey is it?

Suppose not.

They suppose not well, that's about as qualified a success as we've had all year isn't it love, love? Everything, you alright love?

I think I can, would you pull over Sinclair?

Pull over why, what is it, why do you want me to pull over?

That smell again, I'm sure I can smell that smell again.

Really, that smell. Are you sure? I can't smell anything.

Well you never can though can you, what with all those cigarettes going in that mouth I have to kiss. Would you bloodywell pull over?

When I get the chance, I can't just pull over here we'll end up in a bleeding ditch won't we but, yes, would you look at that, I can pull over by the gate can't I now?

I'm just being on the safe side is all I'm doing. Really Sinclair, I knew we shouldn't have gone this way.

Then why didn't you say so love?

Because you never bloody listen do you, never listen to a word I say.

We're not going to get stranded are we? So close to home.

No Christopher, we're, like you say, it's too close to home for us to be getting stranded in any kind of a hurry. It's just, well, your mother's right, it's just the engine is overheating a bit is all that's happening probably. It's just getting over this hill, this hump that's going to be the issue isn't it though?

I'm not so, you know Sinclair, I think we might just be a little heavy is maybe the problem. We might have a bit too much weight for this.

It's all that wine, all that bloody wine you bought in Dieppe.

Language Christopher, besides, it's the wine we should be thankful for, the wine that's got us so far.

It's the wine that's making my legs go numb.

Don't be silly it's, you're only a little cramped and, well, I hope you're not trying to suggest, we can't really go jettisoning the wine, not here any road, so close to home.

It's only you two, only you two that's bloody drinking it.

Language Christopher, honestly. It's me and your father that's paid for this holiday isn't it, if we want to take a little wine home then that's our bonus really, our bonus is all it is.

Paid for this holiday.

We've paid for this holiday and if me and your father.

But how, how's dad gone and paid for it when he doesn't even have a job?

Helen that's enough really take that back. Who do you think it was went to work when you were little, how do you think we afforded this car in the first place, honestly. Without your father there would be no holiday and if we, if me and your father fancy a little wine at the end of a long drive then that's our business, isn't it just?

A little wine?

16

Yes Helen, a little wine. I think your mother might be right, a touch less weight in the back and we'd be making it fine over this hill. What you think love?

I think you might be onto something there Sinclair.

There's a pull-over round this bend.

But Michael's only seven.

I'm nearly eight.

Nonsense, it's only a couple of miles. Your grandpa had me walking further than that to school and before I was seven as well. Anyway, you're in charge Christopher, you'll be able to keep an eye on him, make sure everyone gets back safely. And well, it's only a couple of miles, shouldn't take you so long should it. Just enough for me and your mother to, to have a cup of tea and get to the shops but, not in that order necessarily, I should think we'll be wanting proper milk before we so much as think about a brew.

That we will and, spuds eggs and an onion or two should see us through, there's cheese enough for omelettes isn't there.

Not the sheep's.

I wasn't suggesting the sheep's cheese Sinclair really, what do you take me for?

Are we having omelettes again?

Well, yes sorry love, it's just well, they're quick aren't they, something quick for us to eat?

I like omelettes.

That's good Michael. Now, you're happy aren't you Christopher, sure you know the way?

Yes mum it's, just over the hill. Are you really doing this?

Doing what?

Abandoning us.

Nonsense, no, we're not abandoning you. It's only over the hump and well, think of it as one last adventure, to round the holiday off.

I can't believe you're really doing this.

Just make sure you stay well in to the side, if any traffic comes.

You're really doing it, aren't you?

They're doing it aren't they, leaving us to walk.

Really, we wouldn't be, if there was another option we wouldn't be going about it this way. Christopher's in charge remember. Keep in.

This is, I can't believe they've gone and done this, this is rubbish.

It's not so bad, come on it's, we don't have to carry anything do we.

Have I ever walked a couple of miles before?

A couple of miles isn't even that far Michael. You remember the walk to the refuge?

The refuge in France?

That refuge Michael really, what other refuge have we even been to?

I remember when curtains might contain faces in the night, crowds gathered in the wallpaper. I remember mum when she was tired, that bit of a muddle calling me Sinclair sorry Christopher, Michael, I mean Michael, sorry Michael. I remember starting on twenty pence pocket money and saving up, swapping over for bigger coins, confusion, how one thing could replace, mean the same as five separate, other things. I remember when wallpaper was formed solely of nightmare.

I remember bubble paintings, remember folding paper in half to make butterflies. I remember wearing saucepans for a hat, remember I got a saucepan stuck on my head my mum used up half the butter greasing it off.

I remember being told, it coming up years later how I stopped, made a car slow down so as I could help a ladybird cross the road, remember thinking we might fly away together thinking all the animals might be my friends.

I remember lying in bed thinking why me why do these things always happen to me. I remember waking up on Saturday mornings I would wake up the earliest out of everyone, would wake up come downstairs with the screentest still going some girl playing noughts and crosses with a clown. I remember it would be *Open University* until the cartoons. I remember thinking how funny it would be to trick everyone and put salt in the sugar bowl. I remember it was quiet in Evergreen Forest until Bert

Raccoon woke up. I remember it being time for breakfast and the cereal tasting funny, bowls and bowls of it tasting wrong somehow I thought it was the milk, forgot what I'd done to the sugar. I remember vegetables, the carrots steeped in water oranging to meet them.

I remember a particular peculiar smell to the cars we had, smell of car sickness on moist days. I remember the smell of headaches, wet feet when it rained. I remember coming back from holiday thinking would things ever be the same. I remember but do I, did I really think those things. Thinking would the house be the right way round, be tilted on its axis, furniture on the ceiling like something out of *The Twits*. Thinking it is not the places but ourselves that cannot help from ever changing, not the mirror but the reflection. I remember when we threw the electricity out of the house.

Well, that didn't take so long, did it now?

Suppose not.

We've hardly been back ourselves.

They cheated.

Michael we did not. It always is a, mum what is it when Michael says vegetable in twenty questions?

Was it a Venus flytrap love?

See, how can we even, you need a new vegetable is what you need Michael.

But I like Venus flytraps the best.

That's good Michael, now, how's about we all have a cup of tea, you sit yourselves down before I make a start on these omelettes?

I'll put the kettle on.

Thanks love.

It's always nice isn't it, when you first come home to ceramic. To be drinking from a proper mug again. What with that and the real milk it's a wonder we go away at all. You want a hand with anything love?

Maybe if you, if you were to sit down out of the way might be best.

I'll just give, how about I open these beans? Saves you doing it doesn't it just?

Sinclair really, will you stop fussing give me some space.

I was only trying to lend a hand love.

I know you were but, honestly, if you want to help you can be a help by getting out of my hair for a change.

Tell you what I'll just, how about I open a bottle, give it a chance to breathe.

Isn't it a bit early for that Sinclair?

Well nothing, I wasn't thinking of opening anything fancy just, it's been a long day hasn't it, we've faced its challenges and here we are home again it's something, isn't it, to raise a glass to I mean?

If you insist but, I thought you said you'd allow it to breathe?

It can breathe in the glass, can't it but.

Sinclair.

I'm pouring you one aren't I?

If you were to get some plates ready first. From the cupboard.

I know they're in the cupboard love really, some things I haven't managed to forget. Tea's ready kids.

Oh Michael you look worn out, all that walking on top of an already long day.

Two miles isn't even that far mum.

Isn't it now? Well, you do look tired is all I'm saying. Be near enough straight to bed for you.

Can I read for a bit first?

If you can keep your eyes open I won't be stopping you, now, what do you say?

Thanks mum.

Thank you.

Well, isn't this something then. Sitting round the table the five of us again and, it feels funny doesn't it, at first. All those little adjustments you've to make after camping, getting used to being indoors again. And then before you know it you'll have forgotten what it was like being outside, sleeping in a tent. Still, it was something, wasn't it? A good holiday we had. Something to look forward to isn't it?

What is dad?

Doing it again, next year I mean. Yes, should think it'll have to be next year. Unless we risked half-term.

We are not risking camping at half-term Sinclair.

Suppose not and, well, I was only thinking aloud really. Be good to do something though. We could, I don't know, could think about a caravan maybe. Have more than just a run about for a change. You ready for a, fancy a top-up love?

That was, there's no need to hurry Sinclair.

It's been a long day hasn't it, besides. I'll slow down in course.

Dad's getting drunk.

Are you getting drunk again dad?

Really you two, your father is not getting drunk he's just unwinding after the journey we've had, watch it the pair of you really, I've had about enough of this today.

Sorry mum.

It's not me you should be apologizing to.

What's wrong with it though, if I might happen to fancy a little drink at the end of a long day. If this is the respect I get really, my own skin indeed.

A little drink.

23

And would you even taste it. You know sometimes, all your lives I've thought that this was it, that you were pretty much perfect and I wouldn't want you changing, that if I had the choice and I could have kept you as a newborn babe in the arms or when you Helen had just started talking then I would have done, would have kept you that way forever. But I taste this now, the sun in it, the climate, and if I was to give you a glass then you wouldn't be ready yet to appreciate it, even you Christopher. And there's so much ahead of you, isn't there. Even if you have got exams coming up and there's a job you'll have to be going to in the future, a tie to put on and all those alarms to set, well at least there'll be this, all those things you can't yet appreciate.

I don't think I'm ever going to like the taste of wine.

We'll see about that when the time comes round and, speaking of which, isn't it about time the three of you were thinking about beddy-byes?

Can we watch the telly for a bit first?

What is it, that you were thinking of watching?

The telly dad.

In that case certainly not I mean really, not even knowing what there is to watch.

But dad.

Don't you but dad me.

I remember when a can of pop wouldn't ruin a quid. I remember a certain confusion regarding the phrase fit as a butcher's dog, surely eating all those offcuts offal intestines the dog would be a fat lump but no, it ran alongside the butcher's van kept in good shape. I remember being surprised that man-size tissues were not so large as bed sheets not big enough to contain an adult human. I remember when Helen was at primary school we would walk down together holding hands through the park but when she went to South Craven I was all by myself would walk down alone. I remember running, wherever I went I would hurtle towards it.

I remember thinking to be struck by lightning would be to be granted awesome powers. I remember wanting to be struck by lightning.

I remember a blue tit I think it was a blue tit. I remember finding a dead bird in the garden it had flown into a window, been taken by a cat. I remember taking it upstairs being found later on the landing, stroking, that I was stroking the blue tit as I plucked away its feathers, saying poor birdie, poor birdie as I plucked it back to meat.

I remember lying in bed thinking why me why do these things always happen to me.

The mechanics of it.

I remember what's black and white and red all over. I remember several incarnations of Robin Hood, remember

Robin Hood as a fox as a man, different men. I remember on a walk once losing a shoe having to be carried, on the way back down it had been placed, someone had placed it on a stile for safe finding. I remember always, ever after calling it, that the walk was called Michael's Shoe Walk from thereon after. I remember in the night noises bending into shapes, scared awake in the night being made a cup of milk. I remember wanting to be carried how I wanted to be carried. I remember the defence systems of several dens were profoundly reliant on being attacked from below. I remember what's black and white and read all over, I remember shark-infested custard.

I remember feeling new in the village, feeling outside it foreign even for coming from another part of Yorkshire, remember we moved up in term time a weekend but no that can't be right. I remember the village kids saying learn. We're learning him to play football, learning him to catch. I remember I'm not sure if I did like football if I really liked football remember teaching myself to try and like football so that I might join in. I remember packed lunches, remember being jealous of the kids got crisps always wanting a packet of crisps. I remember when the better part of a day could be spent making a dam.

I remember watching *Open University* learning about flying squirrels when my parents woke up I was full of questions they hadn't even had a cup of tea.

I remember getting the terms psoriasis alopecia and cirrhosis mixed up, confused.

I remember asking who the Queen of Sheba was being told she was a lady had too many presents.

I remember an interest in topiary, remember several months when I wanted to be a topiarist, thinking I might be a zookeeper, be an inventor instead.

I remember lying in bed thinking why me why do these things always happen to me. I remember thinking why do these things happen through me why not Helen not Christopher, thinking why is it me, this thought inside me, in my head not elsewhere.

I remember when dad cooked him saying king of the microwave lord of the rings over and over again. I remember burnt chicken chicken charred black on the outside red in the middle, fag packets thrown on the barbeque catching orangreen electric in flames.

I remember tirrick tirrick Arctic tern remember watching a documentary once about Arctic terns and dad came up with something he called it a game, dad mildly shrieking Arctic tern tirrick tern, tirrick tirrick Arctic tern pretending to dive-bomb like terns at a breeding colony his fingernails the beak. I remember tirrick tirrick Arctic tern it being a week or two he played his game. Arctic tern tirrick tern, Arctic tirrick tirrick tern. Pretending to dive-bomb, fingernails as beak. I remember one holiday dad's medication disagreeing with the heat him coming on with a bad case of ~~cirrhosis alopecia~~ psoriasis remember Spain's endless shower of dandruff the terrace of a cafe vultures overhead his scalp flaking in chunks. I remember in the barber's once some kid having nits we never saw him again.

That's not very nice Michael, to go telling stories like that.

But it's true mum, the barber started and he said he couldn't carry on because of the nits in the boy's hair. Isn't it true Christopher it's true isn't it, about the nits?

Mum he said he couldn't, that if he were to carry on then he'd risk an infection and he couldn't go risking that, said it wouldn't be worth his damaging the business if the nits were to spread.

Well even so it's not so, that's not very nice is it, to enjoy someone's misfortune like that?

But it's true mum.

Look I don't really, couldn't particularly care if it's true or not. You wouldn't want to think that someone was telling stories like that about you would you now?

But I, we don't have nits do we though?

Not at the moment you don't but you never know do you and really, I don't know, watch your step.

Dog mess.

Poo.

Dog poo.

Well, I'm glad you've noticed but, there's no reason to form a choral society about it. Oh, it'll be nice. To put this shopping down have a cup of tea and, I was thinking, how do bacon butties sound?

Bacon butties.

Glad they've met your approval but, there's your father now what is he, what is your father. Oh bloody hell Sinclair what is it that you are even doing now?

Where's that other car from mum?

You've taken the words from out of my mouth.

It wasn't, was it there when we left the house?

No Michael it, that car was certainly not there when we left the house.

Why is it missing its wheels?

Well I'm sure there's a perfectly good, perfectly rational explanation which your father will be only too glad to. Sinclair really what, what in the world are you even really, what is even going on Sinclair?

I was just swapping this, just going to get this jacked up and try and prop it with these bricks so as to get these wheels swapped over.

Sinclair you haven't unpacked even started unpacking have you, honestly, what are you even doing Sinclair?

Like I said it's, I thought I'd make a start on this make a little headway is all.

I can see that much Sinclair, honestly.

Well what, why did you need to go and ask me for then?

Because, this bleeding car is why Sinclair. It's not as if it was here when I left you to do the unpacking get the tents on the line, when you sent me out to do the shopping is it Sinclair?

Not when you put it like that love, no.

Where's it appeared from?

You might well ask.

Asking is just what I'm doing Sinclair.

Ask away then.

I already have asked Sinclair really you, you're managing to be more obtuse than bloodywell usual what is going on, where has this thing even come from Sinclair?

That's a, a good question love and, well yes, it's funny you should ask see, I was just getting a coffee on and there was this knock, this guy knocked at the door said he was passing.

Passing Sinclair?

Yes love he, he said that he was passing and.

We live in a cul-de-sac Sinclair.

Be that as it may he just happened to be, just I don't know he just saw the car on the drive and happened to, thought it was worth pulling over I suppose.

Sinclair, honestly.

Well love it's, I was just making coffee and like I said there was this knock, this guy said he was passing and noticed, happened to notice the car and thought, well, you can see what he thought can't you love?

And I suppose you thought the same.

Not in so many words I didn't we, he knocked and pretty much came straight out with it I, it wasn't what I'd been expecting when I put the coffee on but we talked it over and I thought maybe, it might actually make a deal of sense.

Sinclair who even was he?

He didn't give me his life story if that's what you mean.

You know full well that's not what I meant Sinclair, honestly this, this I don't know, you make him sound like a ghost appears out of thin air and he happens to be driving the same car as you just happens to fancy giving it away I mean really, where did he even get to?

I'm not sure he, it's not like he gave a forwarding address love.

That's not the, Sinclair how did he even get away, get going I mean.

He was, left on foot love.

So, let me. A stranger drives up, materializes out of nowhere out of the ether and abandons his car with you, just walks away from this wreck and you didn't even, did you even think to take his name Sinclair?

Oh what does it matter love he was just this guy, some chap who happened to be passing happened to be driving an Escort same as me and he happened to, just saw ours here on the drive and thought, thought maybe we could do a little business is all he was.

A little business?

Yes love, a little business.

Sinclair you are not telling me you paid money for this I don't know this, this, this thing are you Sinclair?

Well he was hardly going to give it away now was he love?

Sinclair how much?

It was only, not much only about, about one-twenty love.

Don't you one-twenty me Sinclair how much?

Well around one-twenty like I said, maybe a smidgen more but.

Sinclair how much did you pay for it Sinclair?

It was one-fifty love.

Oh bloody hell. What were you thinking?

What does it look like I was thinking I mean all I'm doing is I'm going to be using it for parts is all, getting more out of the other I mean don't think about the one-fifty so much, think about how much we're saving, how much a new car would be costing us.

A new car.

You know what I mean.

Honestly Sinclair.

What love this is, I can't see what the problem is here love.

Really Sinclair I don't know, we're lumbered with this thing and where's it going to, I suppose we're going to have it collapsing out the front aren't we just.

Well it'll lend a certain ambience create a bucolic air won't it love. You always did say you wanted to live on a farm.

There's an answer for everything with you sometimes Sinclair.

Why not love I mean not a farm then, look at it, only yesterday the car was carrying us as together we came home became a religion together and here it is today, entering into its second coming, itself being reborn. There's a certain amount of poetry to that isn't there, when you stop and think.

Sinclair really.

What love it's, look at the Buddha I mean that tree, the Buddha wanted a bit of shade get the sun off his back so he sat under a tree didn't he, became a religion that way but the tree itself, well it's not the same tree standing there now as what he sat under how could it be it's been chopped down replanted, chopped down replanted.

Sinclair what are you.

Bear with me love all I'm saying is, this car our vehicle. Behold! My Ford Escort Mark II estate, in whom I am well pleased. This way, if it were to happen that it does become a shrine or a temple, some place of pilgrimage is all I mean. If it does become a place that people want to leave donations then this way, with the car up and running it wouldn't be like, as if we'd have to stay confined, wouldn't be like Stonehenge or the Blarney Stone or I don't know, Walsingham having to stay in the same place would it now. This way we could, if we want to go to the Pyrenees then the pilgrims can follow in our wake, gift currency wheresoever we may be.

Sinclair give it a break really it's.

What love I'm only.

Sinclair, honestly, give it a rest.

All I'm saying is we can still go camping love.

Well that's all well and good but, I've been all around the village been on my feet all morning been carrying these bags and you haven't even touched the unpacking haven't so much as offered me a cup of tea Sinclair.

My hands are a bit mucky love.

I suppose it'll have to be me then won't it.

I remember mugging footballs from the park at break time. I remember the paddling pool was filled by a redirection or channelling of the beck and occasionally in winter or otherwise periods of heavy rain or leaf fall it would fill up of its own accord, all drainage blocked. Once after school in the rain in the winter the general dare went out to run through the murky waters and a boy went for it and fell over, ran off in tears. I cannot remember if this boy was me or someone else but from how the memory seems formed I think it was most probably someone else.

I remember there was a building on the outskirts of the village they called it the Red Barn, it wasn't really a barn and it wasn't really red. I remember bullheads. I remember stickleback, in the summer skimming stones down the beck.

I remember the football pitch in the park, remember my surprise that it did not represent the universal measurement. I remember one time working out that because football pitches can be within a certain or acceptable range estimations as to how much rainforest got lost in a certain year might have been out by a measurement of Wales or even more. I remember a lot of buses could get inside Wembley Stadium. I remember arguing foxes aren't actually brown.

I remember bubble writing. I remember wanting to be an Ewok have an Ewok for a friend.

I remember struggling with the word cutlery and remember it was either like or not like cuttlefish but it taking me years to remember which. I remember parcark.

I remember one time being off school and dad making tomato soup with a cheese sandwich for my lunch. I dropped the cheese from out the sandwich somehow and my disappointment was replaced by my word was it ever replaced by finding the cheese all melted at the end of the soup. I remember a lad in my class got five pounds a week he spent it all on sweets.

I remember an unsubstantiated unease concerning the Red Barn, it was haunted you weren't supposed to go near the place. I remember it was a murder murder/suicide or some form of ritual sacrifice that was said to have occurred there. A boy in my class said his brother went in once found a still-beating pig's heart just sitting on the floor pulsating. His brother was at South Craven was hard but it shitted even him up. I remember at South Craven the big school they said that first years were allowed to smoke in lessons that there was a sixth-former so hard the teachers called him sir, kids who ate coins just chewed them up, a girl with a prosthetic arm made from regurgitated currency. I remember being nervous/scared/nervous about the prospect of having to go there even if it was years ahead.

I remember imagining envisioning untapped powers in a variety of airborne martial arts.

I remember in summer sometimes reading through a crack in the curtains even though it was after lights out. I remember it was three books at a time you could get out on a children's ticket you could keep them up to three weeks, I remember looking forward to the possibilities of an adult ticket jealous of Helen and Christopher thinking what might be done with some of that. I remember first needing glasses and thinking shit this is my own fault. I remember how often glasses would get broken having to play sport, frames mangled and corrected but remaining all askew. I remember not having a video, it wasn't fair, and my dad saying how many times we are not having a video, will you just this once think about the world outside yourself, think about the world outside yourself for a change?

I remember the smell of Imperial Leather soap. I remember sharing the water bath time on a Sunday because I was the youngest I went in last.

I remember blowing up juice cartons with the straw and if there was sufficient juice still inside it would squirt out as the carton deflated. I remember the sensation of having water in the ear was only slightly but nonetheless qualitatively different from the sensation of having juice in the ear. I remember mugging a ball back from a neighbour's garden looking up ball in my hands to catch him in the eye he was still wearing his dressing gown middle of the afternoon.

I remember one time of frogs, a family outing to a nature reserve, some marsh or such a place where there happened to be a fun run going ahead. Squashed flat, emergent frogs squashed down flat. I remember I drew a picture which was contained within the envelope containing the family's resignation from the Wildlife Trust. I remember I came up with the slogan FROGS ARE WILDLIFE TOO.

2

In South America there was a type of sloth that didn't live in trees like sloths do now, a ground sloth as large as a hippo.

Was there now?

There were guinea pigs that big as well, even bigger maybe.

Were there really?

There were yes they, there was all sorts of megafauna in South America.

Well I never it's, sounds to me that you've learnt, pretty much learnt your whole book already.

But I'll have to take it back soon.

There are other books you know Michael, really, change out of your school shoes. Let's go out for a walk.

But I want to read my book.

We don't need to go so far just round the block'll do. While the weather's, we've got the weather for a change. There's plenty of time for reading before tea.

But I've been looking forward to it.

It's not like we need to be so long really, say yes for a change, say yes to life. It's only ideas won through walking contain any worth.

I've been missing it.

It'll still be here when you get back it's, say yes this once to life, the air'll be good for you. Get your shoes changed while we've light enough, I've been saving this walk, waiting all day for you.

Are you messing with me?

When have you ever known me to joke it's, are you going to be doubting me as well now. I don't know it's, once I've fetched the paper, had a look at the washing-up. Once I've read the paper, made a mess of the crossword, what is there. What more can there be, for a man to be looking forward to.

You don't have to wait for me dad.

Well no but, with you to walk with me. That's something, isn't it, to spend a day looking forward to.

Should I change my trousers as well?

It's not as if it's so muddy out and, the clocks'll be turning soon let's make the most of it, say yes why not, if we get out now we can be back in good time for your mother getting home.

What will the others do?

I think they should know where to find a key by now you think, will you be warm enough like that?

You said we were only going round the block.

That we are but, it might be worth bringing your coat just in case. You never know. I thought if we were to walk the top way we could look down on the Clough, see the colours and look back down.

Not the hill.

It's not so big a hill Michael, not for a growing lad like you. Be gone inside five minutes be a shame to miss them, wouldn't it?

Miss them?

The colours.

Colours?

Yes the, the colours yes. It's something isn't it, this time of year. They're only with us, here a few weeks if you're lucky and it doesn't take more than a breath, first breath of wind and then they're gone.

They are nice.

There you go then. It's not so bad, is it now?

No.

You'll be telling me you're enjoying yourself next.

It's only a walk dad.

Only a, best not to get too carried away I suppose. How many are there, do you think?

Colours?

Not so much colours but shades of, gradations within, between the colours.

Down there?

In the Clough.

I don't know it's, there is a lot of them. Yellows and reds. Oranges.

Do you think, you know I wonder sometimes, whether it would even be possible to count them all.

There are a lot. Yellowy oranges and orangey yellows, cadmium maybe. I think, would you call that cadmium there?

Cadmium I, I've got to confess I'm not really sure.

Is that carmine?

Well it might be, but.

What about crimson?

That sounds, I'd have thought that sounds about right.

Crimson there and is that, I think that's burnt umber.

If you say so.

Or ochre maybe, it might be a shade of ochre actually.

I think I'd call that copper if it was up to me.

No it's, copper's more shiny than that.

Shiny?

Copper's shiny dad.

Well that's put me in my place.

Copper's shiny it's, you could keep counting forever almost.

But there were world enough.

If you didn't have to go to school.

I thought you liked school?

I didn't say I didn't.

That's good but, sometimes. You know I sometimes think. Even if you could do that, if you had a day, the whole week off school, were able to count them all and they all had a name, something you could point to it would be, that a little, something might get lost that way, that even if you were, could count long enough to be able to count them all then there wouldn't necessarily be so much, all that much to be gained. If you see what I mean.

Dad I, I'm not sure I do.

Just that it's nice, sometimes. It's nice isn't it, to preserve a bit of mystery. This time of year, these few weeks we're having now, before the frost and light enough yet for a walk after school, all those colours down there, burnt umber if you want to call it that, it doesn't matter, doesn't matter if you chose to call it ochre instead but, I'll get the gate, to preserve a bit of mystery, not have everything known.

You can still see them dad.

That you can but, to appreciate them I mean. You can appreciate them without, don't have to know their names, that sometimes, some things get lost in too much knowing.

Too much knowing?

Just that, it's good to know things, always good to know things isn't it but, if you did know everything, all the names. If you knew everything there wouldn't be anything left to learn and what, would you still want to go to school if you didn't have, there wasn't anything left to learn?

I'd still want to see my friends.

There is that but, that's good, yes. Just, I don't know. To keep a bit of mystery going. You know I do love the summer, sitting with a barbeque sound of ice-cream vans on the air, the evenings all ahead and the smell, you can smell it can't you the summer but, now, all of this now and with the first breath of wind it'll all soon be gone I'm not sure you can, if they've even got a word for that.

Will we miss *Neighbours* dad?

Not you as well. You and your, all of this the leaves on the trees and I've got you, you're thinking about bleeding *Neighbours*.

But I don't want to miss it.

You won't be missing it really.

I don't want to be left out.

41

You won't be getting left out, trust me this once. How about, I could show you a bird's nest if you like.

A bird's nest?

Up there in the ivy.

I'm not sure that's allowed.

Not allowed?

You're not supposed to go near bird's nests, I don't think they like it.

Well aren't you the sensible one it's, we, I wouldn't have thought we need to fret about that any more.

Why not though it's, you're not supposed to.

Maybe not and, don't you be doing it without me, don't go telling all your friends just, it should be long empty by now. The birds will be well away, be sunning themselves in Africa, taking a break by the Med. Here I'll, if you lend me your shoulder.

Dad it's, you're too heavy dad.

It's only so I can get stood up.

Dad.

If you insist I don't, suppose I'll have to pull myself up won't I then.

Be careful.

I'm only climbing a tree Michael, it's not like I haven't done it before. Will you, what do you think about that?

Can I hold it?

If you're, it's very delicate you'll have to be gentle.

It's so light.

Well, what do you think it's made of?

There's feathers in it, bits of moss.

I did think you might appreciate it.

Can I, if the birds aren't coming back can I take it home with me?

Only if you, you don't want to be making your friends jealous.

I won't tell anyone.

That's good yes, aren't you the sensible one. Good to have you on board. It's what we used to do, when we were your age. Go out climbing trees and looking for bird's eggs.

I don't think that's allowed.

Not any more it's not, but. We didn't know any better, would go out collecting bird's eggs. You had to make little holes in them and blow through with a straw.

Dad you shouldn't of.

It was, we didn't know any better, didn't think it would do any harm. You had to be very careful about how you went about it. I used to keep them in cotton wool.

Cotton wool?

They could be ever so delicate, birds' eggs. One time I found a wren's nest and, you know how small a wren is, the eggs were so tiny I was shaking when I picked them up. The eggs were so, I didn't know how to carry them, didn't want them to break so I held my tongue up and put them under it, held the eggs beneath my tongue.

Like this?

I got some funny looks when I was walking home, couldn't say hello to people.

How old were you?

I'd have been, at a guess I'd have been a year or two older than you are now.

Did you make it?

I managed to get them home but they were so delicate, tiny little things. I think I broke all but the one of them when I was blowing out the insides.

So you took them for nothing?

If you put it that way.

You shouldn't have done it.

No but, you are right you know but, we didn't know any better back then, when I was your age. Everyone used to do it. I didn't ever try taking wren's eggs after that. Keep it straight.

It feels kind of soft.

You don't need to keep stroking it, it's not a kitten Michael really, it'll have fallen to pieces by the time we get home.

Are we not?

I thought if we went the bottom way we could make a circle of it, get the most from it all.

Cross the wooden bridge.

We could play, have a game of Poohsticks if you like.

Poohsticks?

Why ever not.

Dad I'm.

Don't tell me you're too old for Poohsticks really, saying I'm not to climb trees being sensible all the time, you can still play games with your father Michael.

It's not even the best bridge for Poohsticks.

Isn't it?

The water it, goes through too fast.

I see what you mean, yes, it's doing a thing or two there. You'd hardly have a chance to be turning your back before it's through, be near enough gone past the bend. Been a nice, we've had a nice walk haven't we though?

Thanks dad.

You wouldn't rather have been reading your book?

There used to be, you got porcupines the size of shopping trolleys once.

Including the spines?

I think so it's, maybe. Actually, I'm maybe not actually sure.

Well you can check in a minute can't you. I bet they must have been very sharp.

You can cut your hand on a modern porcupine even, they're a lot spikier than a hedgehog is.

I bet you could it's, have I ever told you how to go about it, if you ever needed to eat a hedgehog?

I wouldn't want to eat a hedgehog.

Well no but, if you didn't have any other choice.

Would you bake it in clay?

Takes a lot to get past you doesn't it really, I'll have to think of some harder questions for next time. Is that, looks like your sister's home already.

I don't want her to be jealous about my bird's nest.

Well you could hide it behind your back couldn't you, put it safely in your room.

I'm going to keep it on my windowsill.

That's a good idea. Hello love.

Hiya dad.

Did you have a nice day at school?

It was alright I suppose.

Only alright?

Just, it was a day at school dad.

But I thought you were, you barely stopped talking about going back to school when we were on holiday love.

It was I don't know, it was school. School was, it was a day at school dad.

It wasn't so long ago you'd come home and be full of it, what it was you'd been doing all day.

But that was before though.

I'm sorry I'm, before what Helen?

Just, before dad.

Before?

It was when I was at the old school not now, wasn't it?

Oh Helen I'm sorry really it's, that's not something me and your mother want to be hearing you know.

There was, in maths there was a boy and he wouldn't sit down.

At the start of the lesson?

It was all the way through dad.

That's not so, doesn't sound so good love.

The teacher spent the lesson trying to get him to sit down but he wouldn't, the boy wouldn't sit down until after the bell had gone.

Really that's, it doesn't sound a good way for you to be learning.

It wasn't, no.

And what did you, what did you do while the boy wouldn't sit down?

Most of, the rest of the class were mostly talking, were messing about as well but I thought I'd, thought I might as well try and get on with some homework.

That's very diligent of you.

I suppose so.

If it were me I'm not sure I'd, not sure I'd be able to have so much, all your discipline love.

The homework it, needed doing dad.

Well yes but, still. To sit down and be getting on with it, to be getting it done when everyone else, all the rest of the class is talking that's, it takes a bit of doing, takes some discipline that does.

Thanks dad.

Really it's, that does take a bit of doing. Did you get it done?

My homework?

The homework you were getting on with.

Just about.

That is something, isn't it but, is that the door.

Sinclair, honestly now.

Love?

Not this again Sinclair, give me strength.

Sorry love, the kettle's only just boiling.

Not the kettle Sinclair, this. All this again. Give me, what even is it that you've been doing all day Sinclair?

It'll be with you in a minute love just, give it a chance to brew I mean, I've only just switched it on.

Not the kettle Sinclair, this really. Really there's, you've clogged the sink, your ashtrays Sinclair what are the, there's papers all over the floor, how do you scatter your paper so much, your coffee. You've coffee all over the worktop again really, is this really the greeting I'm to come home to every single day?

What it's, I'd have one waiting for you but then you'd only go saying, it would only have gone cold wouldn't it, no one wants to come home to a cold cup of tea, sit you down, put your feet up a minute, you'll feel better won't you for it, five minutes with your feet up and a brew down your neck?

Will you listen Sinclair.

What love it's, sit yourself.

Listen to yourself, please. I don't want to feel better for a brew I want just this once, if only once I were to come home and find you've so much as touched the washing-up, how can a grown man not even touch the washing-up, I don't know.

Really love I'm, sit you down you'll feel better.

I don't have time to sit down Sinclair don't have time to feel better, what have you, don't even tell me what it is you do all day Sinclair.

I've been getting round to it love it's, don't worry yourself so much, I'll have it done, be with you as soon as I've got these poured and, there's space enough isn't there, for you to work round me.

You'll be in my road Sinclair.

But love I.

I don't need you in my road.

48

Love.

I shouldn't have to work round you it's one more thing isn't it, for me to be doing. There's mouths to feed and all this marking, I've got so much marking, didn't get a seat on the train had to stand up till Keighley how can you not empty your ashtrays Sinclair, I mean when, when am I supposed to, it's not as if I'm made of time you know.

3

I remember scraps but I don't remember pea wet. I remember an inflatable tiger all full of helium and tied to the Esso garage on Station Road it didn't last five minutes before someone had popped it with an air rifle. I remember a general concern about the flammability of shell suits. I remember garish colours, Bermuda shorts being a thing, words like cowabunga.

I remember stray coppers, looking for coins on the way down to school. We would pool our resources to buy penny sweets together, remember sometimes the lady in the shop would sometimes give us one two three even extra so we all got the same. I remember penny sweets that looked like bogeys a shop in the village that kept on selling halfpenny sweets.

I remember Queen going from nowhere to favourite band overnight.

I remember one lunchtime the knowledge going round that if you thought about girls with no clothes on thought about the word naked what the word naked really meant then your willy got bigger it really did work. I remember a boy in my class saying he was going to get a tattoo done, that when he was older he was going to get a tattoo on his willy it would be a sad face at first but when his willy got bigger it would be smiling all happy.

I remember the excitement, how excited you could get about a school trip waking up best clothes neatly folded, all dressed in a hurry running jumping the stairs to realize the house was dark it was hours yet till morning.

I remember watching *Tomorrow's World* when CDs were a thing of the future.

I remember Cliffe Castle the bus in to Keighley remember the taxidermy at Cliffe Castle birds of prey glass cases a mangy platypus, words like bicephalic and craniofacial. I remember worsted cloth. I remember Willard Price books, Keighley with Chris. I remember looking for Willard Price books *Amazon Adventure South Sea Adventure*, remember *Whale Adventure* was too much for me back then. I remember that constrictors possess remnant evidence of legs.

I remember cutting my hand on broken glass having been dared to break a window on one of the shelters in the park.

I remember there was a man lived up the Clough for a bit just staying in a tent he said he was going through a divorce just clearing his head. I remember he abandoned the tent or maybe he upped and disappeared when winter happened but either way the tent remained without him there. I remember it was dad who cleared it up after there had been no sign of the guy for a month or so.

I remember a boy in my class was going to get a hoverboard they were being made in Japan. I remember big presents birthday Christmas combined.

I remember spools of cassette tape abandoned on the pavement like bladderwrack on some ever-grey beach. I remember finding it sad that the music was lost would not be listened to, that nobody would listen to that particular slice of music again, remember that sometimes there were some days when I thought the music had been released, set free, better off alone, would not be trapped any more. I remember there were some days the hope and the sadness could not be distinguished, pulled separate from one another.

I remember at South Craven they said a kid wouldn't stop talking and after she'd been told often enough, been told enough times already the teacher slammed her head her eyeballs popped out like actually popped out she was made to spend the rest of the lesson with them staring up from the desk. I remember a peripatetic music teacher who visited primary school made us sing a song about things stolen from jars. I remember thinking did I experience the world the same, did I experience the world as other people what if the colours were more vivid for me what if my reds were their browns what if it was the other way round. Thinking why do these things happen to me my family. I remember knock-a-door run, I remember Bulldog's Charge Bulldog's Charge being banned in the playground. I remember the Argos catalogue.

Look where I'm taking you and seriously you're looking at, which one of you had the bright idea to bring that along?

It's raining dad.

Not so much it's not and anyway, it'd have to be, even if it was bucketing it down you'd still be getting something from out that view.

But the window's stuck.

I don't see what that's got to do with taking that bloody thing here of all places.

We're getting wet.

Dad it's gopping.

Christopher why don't you, oh. I see what's going on.

The road Sinclair.

What about it?

Could you pay it some attention Sinclair?

I am paying attention love.

Not while you're looking over your bloodywell shoulder you're not.

Well next chance I'll pull over and how many times do I have to tell you to put that bleeding thing away?

What thing?

Don't you what thing me young lady you know full well what I'm talking about, pass it here.

But we haven't finished.

I beg your pardon?

It's best thing on every page dad.

Best thing on every, I've heard it all now. Best thing on every page. I don't know just, put it away would you, put it away and take in some of that view.

It's still raining dad.

Less of that, honestly, do I not get a little respect round here put it away.

But we're almost done can we not have five minutes just, five minutes to finish the game?

Five minutes I must be going soft go on then, you can have your five minutes but I'm not, don't think I'm joking if it's not away in five minutes it'll be out, I'll be throwing it out the bleeding window if you're not careful.

Thanks dad.

Not a moment more.

Dad?

Yes love?

It's getting worse dad.

What is?

The window it's, the glass is slipping.

Look I've told you we'll be pulling over didn't I and, you're not, what are you looking at jewellery for?

Because it's best thing on every page dad. That's the game we're playing.

I give up really, I take you here over the moors and pretty soon we'll be able to see the, I'm pretty sure I can smell it already the sea, I take you here and all you want to do is look at that bleeding catalogue really. I despair. Three minutes.

Do we not have four?

Three and a half but, anyway. I don't know why you're even bothering with it why you even think you should have to choose. If we pull this one off we'll be buying, it won't be a case of buying the best thing on every page it'll mean buying all the catalogue the whole bleeding company if you should feel so inclined.

Not again Sinclair.

Not what again love really, that's just the kind of attitude we don't want around this, the sort of thing'll be holding us back from the start.

Really Sinclair.

What?

All I'm saying is don't, that we shouldn't be planning how to spend our windfall just yet.

You and your doubts seriously, what could go wrong?

Where do you want me to start?

You could try the beginning.

Honestly, Sinclair I've had it up to here with this, this, I'm not sure I want to do it the justice of calling it a scheme, had it up to here with you and your abstractions today.

You're going to have to be a bit more specific than that love.

It's just that it, it's all sounding a bit conceptual.

That's just it though isn't it though, that's the very beauty of the, the beauty of it hot. It is, at this stage it is a bit on the as you say conceptual side and that's why we'll be getting, why we should be able to go getting it at a reasonable kind of price.

And what then Sinclair?

What do you mean what then?

I mean what then what, what will we do with it when we've got it then?

Once it's ours?

Once it's ours, yes. Exactly what are we going to do with it then?

Well that's sort of besides the point isn't it love?

Besides the point?

That's not really the issue so far as I can see it. Once it's under our possession it's ours isn't it, doesn't matter so much what we do with it then. Wait on it I suppose. Sit on the investment till it comes to fruition.

Sinclair you're not listening to a word I'm saying, I'm asking, what I'm saying is what's the use, what even will it be useful for?

Your guess is as good as mine love.

Sinclair.

Like I said it's sort of besides the point isn't it. I don't know, can't quite foresee the uses of the material but that hardly means, doesn't mean there won't be any does it now?

So, let me get this straight. You're suggesting we spend what cash we haven't got lying around on something that doesn't even necessarily exist, something that isn't necessarily there and has no, that's got no bloody use?

No bloody use? It's holding everything, keeping the universe in one piece is what it's bloodywell doing and if it's doing that then it must be, there's got to be other uses to which you could put it. Prime numbers I mean. Prime numbers, prime numbers get up to much more than just being indivisible, simply standing up for themselves don't they now.

Prime numbers?

Prime numbers yes but, not prime numbers no then. Not prime numbers so much as the uses of the, just because I can't yet see the uses of the stuff is hardly the issue. Look at it this way for a change look at bronze for instance. Nobody would have seen the potential in that before it was discovered would they now, nobody would have guessed the uses it might be put to.

Bronze Sinclair?

Well I don't know, the wheel then. Nobody could have guessed the possibilities of that when it was being posited, still on the drawing board.

This is hardly the bleeding wheel Sinclair.

Not now it's not no but then again neither was the wheel was it, nobody could of, people must have baulked at the potential in that mustn't they?

People baulked at the wheel?

Well they must have, certain, people must of baulked. Certain people like, people like I don't know, people like you.

People like me Sinclair?

Yes people like you the cynics the naysayers.

People like me Sinclair?

Yes the naysayers yes.

Sinclair.

Yes love?

Would you pull over Sinclair?

Pull over, why do we need to pull over love?

The window.

What window?

For Pete's sake Sinclair could you only concentrate on what's going on for a fucking well change? The one in the back, the one you said you'd pull over to try and fix. The fucking bleeding window Sinclair.

There's no need to get worked up love.

I am not getting worked up.

If you say so.

Sinclair I am not.

If you insist but, you can keep your seat belts on. We won't be stopping long.

It's stuck dad, the glass is stuck down like that.

So I see and, who's been fiddling, for it to get like this then?

Nobody's been fiddling it just.

Christopher did it.

I wasn't fiddling dad I just, just wound it as normal and it sort of let go, slipped out of place like that, dropped down.

I'll believe you if thousands wouldn't.

Can you fix it?

I'm just having a look.

But, it's raining dad.

It's gopping.

We're getting soaked.

Be that as it may I don't think there's much I can rightly do to mend it now it's just, like you say the whole thing seems to have slipped out of place somehow and I can't, for the life of me I can't seem to get it to move back up. Not to worry.

Not to worry Sinclair?

But it's, we're soaking dad.

Be that as it may I, I might, should be able to muster something up.

What are you thinking?

That we might be able to get by with a, that the problem might not be so insurmountable for now.

How so?

Well it'll have to be electrical tape but, so long as nobody fiddles with it we should, it should go about keeping things in place until.

A plastic bag Sinclair?

What else is there it's, why not. Things'll be just about watertight won't they and, it's only till we get back isn't it, look for a more permanent solution.

Such as?

Well I don't know, if needs must we could always, swapping doors over might prove the simplest thing.

Are we going home dad?

Home? Why would we be, who said anything about going home?

You did dad, just now.

Did I no, you must have misheard I, we're not turning back for the sake of a window not being quite right.

But it, dad it's cold already dad.

This is embarrassing please.

Look it shouldn't be too far now and you'll just have to, maybe put your hats on to be getting on with really I don't know, that catalogue, what did I say about that bloody catalogue?

Dad it's.

Pass it over.

But dad we.

I said pass it over. Good.

You're not chucking it dad please.

Don't be silly no, I'm just, only putting it in the boot for safekeeping's sake.

While you're there Sinclair.

Yes love?

You couldn't dig out a blanket could you?

What for?

I don't want them getting cold Sinclair.

But it's only.

Michael looks like he's about ready to start shivering Sinclair really, what's the point of going away if they're going to catch a chill doing it?

Where is it love?

I can't remember where I packed it you'll just have to, have to have a rummage.

Is it, do you mean this one?

Course I mean that one Sinclair give me strength, what other blankets do we ever take with us?

I was only asking love really. Anything, anyone need anything else from the boot?

I shouldn't think so.

If you're sure.

Course we're sure Sinclair really it's a wind tunnel in here, could you please just get it shut.

I was only asking love.

Dad it's, it's freezing dad.

My teeth are chattering.

Michael don't be so silly really, they are not.

It doesn't sound that way from here Sinclair.

He's only putting it on I don't know, we'll be on our way near enough won't we see, that's going nowhere is it you lot, I don't know what it is with you lot going soft. We can't have you being soft if we're to get this up and running.

Sinclair.

Yes love.

Give it a rest Sinclair.

I haven't said so much as a.

It's what you're about to say isn't it though Sinclair.

Which is?

You know full well.

Enlighten me.

You're twisting things again aren't you.

Twisting things?

Yes twisting things yes. Dragging us back to that bleeding notion of yours.

And what's wrong with that love, what's so wrong with wanting the best for you and the kids, us as a family?

The realms of the feasible Sinclair really, you can want for the best and still keep things within the feasible you know.

Oh ye of little faith. Don't be so, open your mind stop being so negative for a change. You've got to speculate to communicate after all.

Accumulate Sinclair.

Yes love, communicate.

Sinclair you're, you're not even listening to yourself Sinclair.

Am I not?

Really Sinclair, I give up.

What love, we've to communicate haven't we.

No it's, that's not the saying Sinclair. It's, you've to speculate to accumulate haven't you though.

What do you even take me for love but, same difference isn't it though.

They're different words Sinclair.

It's not as if words can't go changing love really, what's the difference. Don't be so close-minded this once. You've to accumulate to communicate haven't you, got to communicate to accumulate.

I give up.

You know what I mean don't you though, besides. You're changing it aren't you, clouding my meaning to change what I'm trying to say.

Which is exactly what Sinclair?

The proposal.

I think we've heard about enough about your bleeding proposal for now Sinclair.

Fine-tuning though and, well, so that we've all got things clear. Anything, you got the plan, need to know any more in the back?

Like what dad?

Like I don't know but, it's for the best we all have sufficient grip on this one. Pretty soon, when there's wheels in motion there'll be people coming round, asking all kinds of questions and it'll be for the best won't it, that we're all in the clear.

Dad?

Yes love?

What is it exactly?

What's what exactly?

This, what is it really, this matter you're talking about, that you say we're going to be investing in?

Well it's, that's a very good question actually Helen.

You can't answer can you Sinclair?

Listen to you baulking again no, yes I can give her an answer, honestly. What do you take me for. The short answer is dark matter. That's the answer, in two words there. That for the moment they call it dark matter and, well, nobody quite, they haven't quite answered as to just what it is quite yet.

Who hasn't dad?

The scientists I suppose, physicists or cosmologists or what have you, the mathematicians. From what I can gather it's, well you've got ordinary, everyday matter which is just stuff really, the stuff that makes up the car and us here in it, this view in front of us and seagulls and I don't know, stars and planets and the Van Allen belts and interstellar gases and all that carry-on. So, you've got all that right, all that ordinary matter.

Is France ordinary matter dad?

Yes Michael, France is ordinary matter yes.

Are mantis shrimp?

I don't see why not. See what happens is when they, when the scientists add it all together they, when it's all of it added together and they, I don't know, it's, the detailing of this sort of eludes me but, they kind of have to multiply it by gravity or take the gravity away from it all and, well it's not so important just what they do but when they do it it's, they find that things don't quite add up. You got me?

Sinclair you don't, can't understand this yourself.

But that's not so important is it love, from what I've managed to gather it's, well. All that matters is that when they do the sums it doesn't, things don't quite add up unless you include dark matter in the equations. And well, I don't suppose that's explained things entirely but I don't know, you should be getting the picture at least.

Is it maths dad?

Sorry Christopher?

Is it just maths then dad, the investment?

Christopher stop humouring him, there isn't going to be any investment, please.

No need to be like that love but, no Christopher not quite. See the thing is they know it's there, the scientists know it's under us but they haven't quite, haven't yet found conclusive proof of it so that's, that's the beauty of it I suppose. That's where the treasure's buried, the pot of gold at rainbow's end. Because they don't know exactly what it is we should get, be able to be getting a reasonable price for it.

The more you try the less sense you're making Sinclair, honestly, just give it up would you.

Well I don't know how about, if we were to look at this slightly, take a different angle on things. Say you bought land over there say, that scrappy stuff towards the coast and, well because it's scrappy you got it at a reasonable price, see? And then suppose it was found out that I don't know, some valuable mineral or ore or what have you was deposited within that land, you'd have speculated to communicate then wouldn't you?

Dad?

Yes Helen?

Why don't we just buy some land then dad?

Because it's too expensive and, that's besides the point isn't it? Are you all, do you all have to be against me on this one. My flesh and blood indeed. My own very bones. How about you Michael, have you given up on me as well?

What are we going to do with it dad?

Sorry Michael?

When it's ours, where are we going to keep it I mean?

Good question yes, where are we going to keep it. Because it's everywhere, deep in the mine and, who knows really, what would happen if you were to go moving it about, kept it somewhere for safekeeping. I mean look at that over there the sea look at it. Just suppose if you were to, we had ownership of that seawater over there.

This is getting a bit.

Hear me out love. Say you owned all that over there, the sea as far as the eye can, can look. So far as the field of

66

vision spans. Say you owned all that and wanted to move it somewhere, where would you go keeping it I mean? Where would you find a cavity enough to store all that? But with this it, well it's so tiny they haven't found it properly yet and so, who knows, you might be able to pack it down into a film canister even.

Dad?

Yes love?

I thought you said it was holding everything together, keeping things in place?

Yes?

So wouldn't things fall to pieces without it being there?

Well that is a good point love yes I, hadn't quite thought of that one, but. We'll have to think it through some more and, yes well, that's why we've got you on board isn't it?

I thought this was a family business dad?

Well yes but, that doesn't mean you're guaranteed a job does it I don't think, no, nepotism will only be getting us so far won't it and, well, it shouldn't mean we're going to have to pull out altogether but yes, it's a good point Helen a good thing you've raised it now, before the contract's written up. Now the issue is I guess, how to move on from this I mean?

Sinclair would you please.

But I'm only.

I know but, there's been quite a lot of it for now and, if you could save some for later maybe.

Dad?

Yes Christopher?

The window it's, the bag's come loose.

What did I say about fiddling with it.

Nobody's even touched it dad it's just come loose, worked itself like that.

Well we'll just have to leave it for now and I'll have another, see what can be done when we get to the place the caravan.

Are we nearly?

By my reckoning it shouldn't be too far and you think, will you be able to manage its being like that another ten minutes say?

Just about.

Good yes, you happy then?

Thanks dad.

Michael? You think you can be brave for ten more minutes?

Why's Michael always the one who's being brave dad?

Because he's the youngest.

Dad?

Yes Michael?

What are we going to do when we get to the caravan?

Oh I don't know, first thing I suppose a cup of tea's overdue and, well, I'd have thought it'd be a tad damp for French cricket but.

I'm going to write my Christmas list.

Really Helen, how many Christmas lists will that be? Can't we leave it at home this once?

I'm going to put down, ask for coloured pencils.

You've quite a lot of pencils already Michael.

Proper artist's pencils though.

Lisa had two versions already by the end of the holidays.

Good for Lisa but, can't we just have a few days off, take a break this once? There's reading and cards isn't there, and if needs must we can always try talking to one another.

Steady on Sinclair.

It was only a suggestion love.

Not like that I mean, would you slow down a little. I think the turning might be coming up.

What's it say on the, what was it the directions said again?

After approximately twenty miles on the A161 you'll come to a dip.

Come to a dip? It's been up and down, undulating all the way love.

Well that's why I said to slow down isn't it, so we might recognize things? It says here we'll come to a dip, a marked dip at the top of which we'll see a white farmhouse set back from the road, you think that might, might be here, coming up?

Well it's hard to say isn't it, hard to see through all this mizzle. What's it say after that love?

It says we'll see a white farmhouse set back from the road and after half a mile there'll be a track coming off signposted, bloody hell, that's it Sinclair you've gone too far, you're going to have to turn round.

I can't just go turning round in the middle of the road love.

I didn't mean to turn round in the road I meant, just that you're going to have to turn around when you get the chance.

Don't worry love.

I am not worrying Sinclair.

If you insist but, we're here to relax aren't we?

Not while we're driving we're not.

Well yes but I mean, we know where we're going now don't we love?

I remember Knickerbocker Glories never living up to the name. I remember finding a Black Widow buried up the Clough my brother thought it might implicate us in a crime said it could be dusted for fingerprints. I remember close your eyes and count to twenty. I remember if Barry Thompson said to jump off a cliff would you do that as well. I remember cuckoo spit. I remember caddis fly larvae.

I remember there were kids at South Craven would take swords nunchakus and other such weaponry in with them, would play sword fighting, play close combat the way other kids played football or smoking. I remember they said there was a kid at South Craven with a crossbow bolt through his neck. I remember thinking neck should be spelt with two ks.

I remember wanting to make things better, thinking if I could only make, if I were to only run away, spend a few weeks away it would stop things, fix the noise. I remember I was going to live up the Clough share nuts with the squirrels make friends with the birds have a robin for a lookout. I remember I did not want to be found did not want to be discovered. I remember thinking about running away all day when I was at school, that I packed my rucksack when I was back home. I remember it had been raining, the ground was all wet I hadn't packed a sleeping bag only thought to bring socks, remember I was barely gone half an hour, they barely noticed I'd been gone. I remember logistics, thinking I would have to get my head round the logistics were I to run away again.

I remember thinking having a better football would make me a better footballer. I remember thinking to leave school would mean being able to spell all the words in the dictionary.

I remember finding two litres of cider left to chill in the beck and presuming it had been left by a yob I poured it away. I remember thinking any assembly of teenagers was a gathering of yobs.

I remember the grammar school was called Ermysted's but because it was a boys' school people called it Spermysted's instead. I remember there was an unusually weedy kid at South Craven who was made to spend a night by himself in the Red Barn and when he got out he could pull girls two years older was harder even than the hardest kid in the year above, as if he had gone through more than just puberty in that place. I remember up the Clough past the top bridge small piles of stones appearing down by the beck the local paper jumping on the story writing something about devil worship.

I remember going round to a friend's house, we were allowed Crispy Pancakes for our tea.

I remember never tig your butcher. I remember every man for him sen.

I remember staring at light bulbs and the blotchy refracting patterns which would remain, maps of continents never to be charted remaining even after you closed your eyes. I remember tongue shocks from oblong batteries.

I remember which hedgerows were the most reliable sites for pornography. I remember breaking into a hut at the allotments, it was stuffed full of porn. I remember the entrance exam one Saturday morning all gathered in a sports hall some kids wearing suits all dressed like their dads. I remember the headmaster from Ermysted's going ballistic at a small boy properly losing it at a child. I remember at Ermysted's they gave you so much homework you wouldn't be able to play out any more I didn't want to go didn't want to have to learn Latin, remember it was mum who sat me down, sat me down and talked me round. I remember one time playing out in the full mugginess of summer and seeing a two-minute downpour it might have been a cloudburst moving towards us, the sheer physicality of our imminent drenching. I remember oysters, an ice cream called an Oyster. I remember Tab Clear. I remember a can of pop called Oblivion which was launched as a tie-in for a roller coaster at Alton Towers. I remember wanting to go to a theme park wanting to go on a roller coaster remember we never once went to a theme park, went to marshlands, visited estuaries instead.

4

Well, here we are. Another year, and older again aren't we all? It seems to me they pass more quickly each time, days so full and barely sometimes with a chance to think, and here I am feeling like it might have been yesterday, the day before yesterday that I was letting you know (of) last year's news. That it is three years since they have all been at school even now surprises me some days.

They continue to do well there. Christopher is starting to think about what subjects he will be taking at GCSE, and seems quite set on/excited by the prospect of dropping French. He is growing at a rate of knots, will soon enough be taller than his father. Helen continues to get very good reports, seems already to be thinking of her future. We tell her she is too young for all of that ~~but will she listen~~, and hopefully she does listen. Michael spent much of the year obsessing over carnivorous plants but seems now to be moving on. It was the mantis shrimp last week, cryptozoology the week before. Who knows what will become of it all/where we will be in another five minutes.

Sinclair.

Who knows really what will become of it all. I think it was only after Michael was born that Sinclair abandoned/accepted/faced the reality that he (might not be able to) was unlikely ever to walk the Great Wall of China or work as a lighthouse keeper (probably). And what of them, our dreams for them? Of course we want the best for them, but who am I to say what that best might (happen to) be? ~~Some days the insects smash against the windscreen so quick there is no moment to catch a thought.~~ We try to set an example, and can you do much more than that?

Sinclair (?)

When people say I wish I'd known then what I know now, I understand, ~~but; I'm not quite sure what it is I really know (I am not so sure what it is to know a thing, what knowing a thing - to know a thing - even means)~~. You do your best with what you're given, and is there any more than that, any more that ever really can be done?

Sinclair is.

The village remains much the same, although we have recently learnt that our nearest shop is likely to be shutting in the new year. The owners are moving from the area and it looks as if it will be converted into housing. With building work all here and there, it does seem necessary, but after the florist's last year it will near enough be two in two. It ~~seems~~ is a nice enough community and to think that we have been here these years already, but we sometimes joke about how long it might take to be accepted by the more local locals. Some days the insects collide so quickly there is no breath in which to catch a thought. Maybe by the time the children have children of their own. The summer fair was good this year, and there have recently been new goalposts put up in the park.

Sinclair is yet to return to work/takes it/I take him day by day/ how to/if only I could get him to do more while I am out at work/I do wonder sometimes, what he does with his days (what I would do if faced with days such as his/days and days such as those he has), ~~how he manages to contain himself from, not gin in the morning so much as~~

76

~~the idea, the entertained notion of gin in the morning~~. But is it/can it be/is it just a case of trying to get through this, doing what can be done with the belief/hope that there will come a better, a better time will come, that at least things cannot remain the same for ever. The world is not the same thing twice. The world is not the same thing twice.

We went to the Pyrenees in the summer holidays. It is quite the drive but worth it once you're there. One night a storm blew through with hailstones the size of actual marbles. Some of the French had fortunately brought spades with them, and everyone joined in to dig trenches round the tents. One or two were quite badly damaged/ripped but we were lucky in that it blew through quite quick. It would have been a total washout had it stayed that way for long. One day we walked to the Spanish border and the children wanted to see how many times they could cross over, how many times they might visit Spain in a single day. They were well into double figures before we succeeded in calling a halt to it. While all three do have their moments, they do keep us entertained/amused/exasperated sometimes. We saw a golden eagle, which everyone enjoyed.

Of course it is no great statement to say we each have one life only, but for my own part/now that I am well into it I do wonder sometimes ~~what might perhaps have been~~. To think of when we first met (first our eyes did meet)/our eyes together across the staffroom. When we went for that first drink after work, he suggested we meet up for a walk. To think back to our wedding day, honeymoon night. That it would come to this/all this was to ~~come~~ culminate. I knew then that what might be might be, but it was always going to be the case of coming to know what that might in actuality turn out to be. The poet Wallace Stevens says it can never be satisfied, the mind. I cannot remember how I came across it, whether it was me introduced it to him or the other way round, but do remember that it was the title that first attracted me to it. 'The Well Dressed Man with a Beard'. Something about that tickled me. When Sinclair came home from work I used to greet him with it ~~until the time he set fire to his tie~~ when we were first married. If I had known then what love might turn out to be. What poems we might come to share.

To think of it that winter just married and moved into our first house, the heating going and us with no money then spare to fix it. To think we have come from that, two months it seemed with breath clarifying (like butter) amongst the air. Those months of it raining and damp/the layers we'd put on and all the knitting I did for him, for us, so we might retain the dignity of not having to wear our coats inside, bring raindrops into the house.

They are the limbs of me. To ~~separate the person from the emotion to separate the emotion from the person the event to separate, I wonder, might it even be//to separate emotion from emotion, unpick detach. When I think of me do I think of me any more when last did I, think of that, me myself, when last did I (put myself first)~~ differentiate. Those Russian dolls, the beauty in them. For me it is not contained in each alone but due to it being the case that, even when apart, the form or the presence of the others, the intimacy of their relationships, seems inherent in each individually, the individuality of each alone. Something complicit. As if they are more than (just/but) themselves (with/because of) the others around them.

But no, it cannot be, the mind it can never be satisfied. Now and these evenings with them up to bed, I do wonder, what will be. With their posters, the Blu Tac sullying the walls, I do wonder. Where love might go next. Because even if it could be/if I had the choice would I wind *them back and keep them at two/three/four, even if I was guaranteed sufficient sleep, would I? Than this, their choices ahead (of them). Of course we want the best for them, but what will constitute that best is for them not me to say. What doors they might open excites/terrifies me together.* ~~As long as they are, as long as they. Happy/mainly happy/ content (mostly).~~ *Looking back it seems so, so (???) but at the time it was, we were starting out together and it was just what had to be. I don't think I even thought of it as/did I think of it, that time then and breath seeming solid enough to cut, the knitting of the jumpers and the two of us warm with each other/did I even think/it was just what love just what marriage was. I knew it wouldn't last forever and you do, don't you, you try and do your best with what you're given. We will most likely make it to the Pyrenees again this summer.*

5

But it's not fair I can't read so well as you.

Don't be silly Michael.

But you're older, just because you're older and can read better, get the answers earlier on the screen.

It's not that we're older it's because we're more, better educated than you. Timotei!

That's it, you're cheating.

How can reading be cheating Michael really, what are you even talking about it's, Bounty! Bounty! It's Bounty actually Christopher.

It was, I saw the coconut and guessed too quick.

But it's not, how can it be fair when I can't read so well as you, it's not fair though is it?

You'll just have to get better at reading won't you then. Daz!

Persil!

No it's, Surf! Surf! Got one, it's Surf!

Just because they said so Michael.

Why's that, how's it any different from you reading it though?

Well don't be getting all big headed about it and Vite.

Vitali.

Vitalite!

That was mine I got there first.

No you didn't it was me, I got there.

I got it.

We all did it was a.

Draw yes, a three-way split.

Head and Shoulders!

Bran Flakes!

Scottish Widows!

How many's that?

I got three.

Well done Michael, you're getting better and, three and four is well, you might catch up. I'm on thirteen and you've got twelve Christopher.

First to twenty?

Why not yes and, see if there's any, if Channel 4's still on the programme.

It'd be good wouldn't it, if they gave you a countdown, some sort of a timer, so you might know when they were next coming up.

What are you three flicking about for?

We, we're playing the advert game mum, I'm catching up.

Whatever next.

Nice one Michael.

What've I done?

Leave your brother alone I don't, neither know nor, don't know don't care whose bright idea this was, honestly, the advert game. Sinclair!

Love?

You might be interested in what your progeny are playing at.

Is that so?

When somebody owns up you will.

We were only playing the advert game dad.

I suppose it's about time one of you got good at something but, all three of them was it?

That's not even the half of it.

You're not telling me there's more?

They weren't even pretending to watch the programmes, were just flicking the channels looking for breaks.

When you think you've heard it all. I don't know. Christopher, Helen. Wasting electricity, allowing it to leak out for the sake of that. Have any of you a single, anything to say for yourselves?

We were only playing.

It's just a game.

I don't know I've really, I've had it up to here with this. Outside. I want the three of you outside now.

But dad.

Don't you but dad me young lady, I've said you're to go outside you can do what you're bloodywell told for a change.

But it's cold dad.

We'll catch our deaths.

Well you should have thought of that before, I don't know, if you're so keen on playing games there's plenty of room out on the street.

It's dark already.

Well what were street lights invented for, honestly, I want the three of you outside for twenty minutes and, you'll be to bed without any tea if you keep this up.

This isn't fair.

Whoever said about life being fair, if life was fair the three of you might go showing an ounce of gratitude really, if you want to be getting your coats on you'd better be acting sharpish.

Sorry dad.

It's a bit late for apologies love, honestly, outside. I'm going to be locking this door and if I get so much as a hint you might be waiting for it to be opened it'll be staying locked, you hear me?

Yes dad.

We're all very sorry.

Nice one Helen.

You're all to blame as much as each other. That means you this time Michael, look lively. Shoes on, outside. Out before I throw you out.

You've heard your father.

That wasn't, I'm not being too harsh on them am I love?

Twenty minutes is hardly enough to go getting a chill is it Sinclair I don't know, they've to learn sometime I don't, I don't bloody know. The advert game.

Whatever next.

Indeed.

Twenty minutes we could.

The table needs clearing.

Or, you know.

Not now Sinclair really, you've had all day.

It's only the table love.

If it's only the table why's it have to take so long?

I don't know I could, always open a bottle.

Is it not a bit early?

Just, to have it breathing and, it is a Thursday love.

Well if it's a Thursday but.

Yes?

There won't be any for later.

Why worry about later when it's now love really, we can worry about later when it comes.

If you say so.

Well I don't know, but. How was it, your day I mean?

Bloody awful since you happen to ask.

Really love that's, what was so bad about it?

Other than finishing my marking on the train and two sets of third years in a row Sinclair, not getting a seat until I was halfway home and having to carry all this bloody marking with me I don't know, where would you like me to start?

Always good to draw a line under these things isn't it?

I'd have thought so but, I thought you said you were going to let it breathe?

It is rather warm in here love.

I suppose so and, thanks Sinclair.

Your pleasure's all mine. Oh it's a, a nice drop that, a steady tipple.

Easy Sinclair.

I've been waiting all day for this love.

Don't feel you've to hold back on my account.

Not the wine love really these days, I don't know how I'd ever get through them if I couldn't look forward to you, you and the kids coming home, don't know whether I'd begin to cope.

You've a funny way of showing it, honestly, if you could only pick up your bloody newspapers really, if you could empty your ashtrays just once in a while.

They've to be kept somewhere love.

Whatever for?

What does it matter love really I mean, they're to hand now aren't they?

To hand?

Well I don't know but, top-up?

I've barely had a chance to touch this one and, slow down would you?

It is Thursday love.

Just because it's Thursday doesn't mean you have to be drunk by teatime Sinclair.

This is hardly getting drunk is it now.

Not yet it isn't but, it needn't be a race and, give us a hand with these carrots would you?

What is it they need?

What's it look like they need draining but, I thought I said to clear the table.

That you did.

Well what's been keeping you.

Oh I don't know it, it only takes a minute doesn't it.

Don't bother.

Love?

There's no time for that now we'll just have to, to have it in front of the telly this once.

If you're sure.

Why not one time's not going to hurt anyone is it and, besides. We have kept them locked out.

We don't want them thinking of it as a reward.

They can think of it as a consolation then and, call them in would you?

Right you are but, look at them the three of them, playing French cricket together. Kids!

Yes dad?

Tea's ready.

Can Helen finish her innings?

I said tea's ready Christopher.

Three more balls?

Alright then but, that's your lot. Well held Michael. Come along now or, we don't want your food growing cold. That wasn't so bad, was it now?

Suppose not.

Well I don't know, having the telly on when there's all the street to be playing out in. If I catch you playing that game again I'm confiscating the bleeper.

Please dad?

Can I not be taken seriously really, this is my home as well you know, honestly, wash your hands would you? I don't know sometimes but, this looks nice.

Thanks Sinclair it's, no. There's cutlery out already.

I hadn't noticed.

Well open your eyes for a bloodywell change.

Mum?

Yes Michael?

Do we need to lay the table?

That's a nice offer but, no. Your father and I thought we might as well eat off our laps this once.

Off our laps?

There's no need to sound so worried I mean, we will be using plates.

That's, I've got the Hot Set. Hot Set!

Give it here.

I got them first.

Give it.

They're mine.

Christopher really, let your brother have his cutlery for once. I don't know it's, I've buttered the vegetables already.

Thanks mum.

We've an eye on you.

Sorry dad.

So you know and, everybody happy?

Thanks dad.

Good and, who's got the whatsit?

Are we, we're watching the telly?

For this once why not but, don't go thinking you can be forgetting your table manners just because we're in front of the box.

Yes mum.

Let's be having some news on then.

Not the news.

Boring.

Less of this, boring really I don't know, if we're having the telly on we'll at least be having something worth its salt.

But it's boring.

I'm falling asleep.

Don't be silly Michael.

You've heard your mother really, will you all just pay attention, think about the world outside yourselves for a change?

But it's.

That's enough now. Switch it over.

There's news on here as well mum.

I said to switch over.

But.

Listen to your mother.

Why though, when it's already on?

Because I, I am not having my children brought up on *ITV News*.

Will you all just, only listen this bleeding well once.

It's not me it's, dad you've sat on it.

So I have but, there you go then. In the nick of time.

Thanks Sinclair.

You about ready for a top-up?

That'll be the end of it Sinclair.

You could always, nothing's to stop me popping out for another bottle.

It's barely six o'clock.

It is a Thursday.

Which means some of us have to be getting up inside twelve hours Sinclair.

You've a way of reminding me sometimes.

I was only making a point.

You only ever are.

Really Sinclair, don't let me be stopping you.

No, no. You've had your say.

Well one of us has to think of your bleeding liver for a change.

No answering, really love there's no answering some of this is there.

I was only.

I'm sure you were.

Really Sinclair.

Mum?

Yes Helen?

What are we going to be having for tea tomorrow mum?

Steady on love I mean, we've barely sat down for this meal yet.

We're not having omelettes are we mum?

I'll confess I haven't paid it too much mind.

We haven't had fish 'n' chips in a while.

That's a thought.

Gives you a bit of respite doesn't it love?

But it won't be omelettes.

It's a little early for ruling things out but I wouldn't have thought so, no. Really though. What's got you, you're not usually so concerned about what's for tea when there's all tomorrow, a day of school to be getting through with first.

The news.

The news?

They're saying there's something, salmolella in the eggs and they're saying the salmolella, that we might go catching it.

Are we going to catch salmolella dad?

No it's a, I'm fairly sure salmonella's a bacteria and you don't, it's not like a virus say, not as if you can strictly go catching a bacteria.

It will make us ill though won't it.

Are we going to, is it serious dad?

Will it kill us?

Are we going to die?

Stop look stop fussing will you the lot of you, honestly. Ignorance and chips. We've said we're having fish 'n' chips but if we weren't, even if we were having omelettes and even if the eggs did have, even if the eggs were to have salmonella in them it's not the omelette you want to be worrying about. Far as I can gather your omelette is a safe enough bet, solid ground. It's your scrambled you want to be watching, your soft-boiled eggs.

No more soldiers?

If you're going to put it like that I'd have to say not, no.

Why not?

Because of cooking, the cooking through of them. If you only, cooking the eggs through seems to be, it's a thorny issue but if you cook them, heat them properly through it shouldn't be, you'll probably be shot of it, nullify the salmonella if there was any salmonella in there to be getting on with.

Make them hard?

If you put it like that.

But they're not so nice without the yolkiness.

It's the best bit.

This isn't fair.

Well I don't know but, live dangerously then. If you really want the yolkiness then you're going to have to live dangerously aren't you just, live that little bit dangerously for a change. If you want to take that risk but, I wonder. If anybody's thought of that, catering.

Catering Sinclair?

Why not I mean, if it's not the eggs it's something else isn't it, where they come from or I don't know, the salad even. They always talk about watching the salad.

Dad I, who's they dad?

Them.

Them?

Them yes, the doctors the lawyers the.

Not the doctors Sinclair, please.

The doctors yes they, they always talk about watching the salad.

Watching the salad?

The salad yes I mean, the water that it's washed in or is it something, that happens to the lettuce.

Sinclair what are you.

Bear with me love I'm only just thinking this but, think about it though. It shouldn't have to be about, needn't be about getting rich per se, rolling in the money getting rich quick or not only that anyway and maybe that's been, maybe that's been the problem, maybe the problem's that we've been looking from the wrong angle, looking the wrong way at the problem all along.

What problem Sinclair?

This I mean it's Thursday isn't it, Thursday evening one day to go but still you can't relax can you, can't put your feet up properly, have to give a thought to how your head'll be feeling come the morning and, there must be mustn't there, some easier way than this I mean.

Sinclair what.

Bear with me I said, honestly love I'm only just thinking but, maybe the idea isn't the issue, maybe it's not about the idea, not about spreading the Rapture or backdating our miracles, the nature of the tax breaks that might be available. Not the idea so much but rather, how the idea goes getting implemented. How we go about removing the obstacles from out of its path.

Sinclair really, what are you getting at?

Paella.

Paella?

Yes paella yes I mean, it's staring us in the face, what you've got going on there. You've got your rice haven't you and your chicken which is a biggie isn't it, the chicken, your chicken is a big one and if that's not enough you've your prawns and

93

your mussels, the shellfish perspective. Give them a side salad and they won't know where to look, attack from all sides.

I like paella.

Not this time you won't.

Give over Sinclair really, what are you even getting at?

A catering operation.

Catering?

Why not I mean, setting up a catering operation and.

I suppose it'll be me does the cooking won't it.

Not necessarily love but.

Where are we going to find the, I don't have time for this Sinclair.

Well make time then I mean, fair means or fowl. Because like I've been saying it's not the ideas necessarily but how we go about implementing them and, look at it this way for a change. The opposition I mean the obstacles the obscurations, stumbling blocks in our way, obstructions on the road ahead.

What obstructions Sinclair are you imagining things again?

No I am not imagining things and, take that back, honestly will you. Love of my life and doubting me again I mean well I mean the naysayers and the petty officials and the moneylenders, forms in triplicate and carbon paper and signatures in need of verification, the dignitaries and the doubters, those many layers holding things back, stifling us. Because you could always go about bribing people but where's the cash for that. And this way I mean it's simple really, if you only think about it. All you need to do is set one up, establish a catering operation and organize some kind of a big meal, a banquet or a feast day yes, all religions have feast days don't they, why not call it a feast day no one's going to go questioning our right to that, call it a feast day and invite them, the ranked officials and the levels of power, our rivals and.

Rivals Sinclair?

Yes love our rivals yes.

What rivals Sinclair?

Them.

Them?

Them love yes, them they, the living bastards them. Don't go telling me I'm the only one's thought of buying his family the universe love, honestly. Give us a bit of credit here. So we get them there, get all them bastards the doctors sat down and they'll be expecting an entrée but I don't know, nothing too substantial we've to leave space for the main and that, that's when you hit, give it to them with the paella and the salad on the side.

But you, you said they'd watch that dad.

Watch what?

The salad.

Not if we say it's a dietary requirement no, no a law yes, no, not if we say it's a dietary law our practice they won't, part of our practice like taking your shoes off before entering a mosque or carrying a sword, what direction the mirror faces when you're having a shave I don't know, even if they did you've got a lot, there's a lot going on you've got the rice, the rice I mean what is it, is it to do with how you cook it or the reheating or, it doesn't matter right now, there's potential isn't there, means to butter things up, grease it along. So you've got them, that's your first blow the initial contact and then there's chicken in there as well, your big man the chicken, it's, well, these things are, far as I know these things are all about the bacteria aren't they, how you allow that, encourage it to multiply, to spread amongst itself and, they'll be on the back foot then won't they, reeling from the quick one–two before the shellfish come into play, enter the arena, the prawns and the mussels brought into contention like an uppercut, final blow to the chin but not the final, no, not the final blow but have them wobbling at least unsteady on their feet because, why stop there though. Why the need to call it a day, go doubting ourselves. There's dessert isn't there to be thinking about give me a minute, I don't know what about, how about if we were, took blancmange as a starting point.

Blancmange?

Blancmange why not, it's worth looking into anyway. There's milk in that isn't there or cream is it I don't know, it's a dairy element at least and there must be mustn't there, some means of doing a thing or two about that. Next time we're at the library can everyone try and remember to have a look, see if they've anything on the theory of blancmange. What else is there I mean, if we were to give them a choice of desserts, how about, is there potential in meringue perhaps?

Not if you were to get it to set.

Dad?

Not while I'm thinking.

Are we going to be killing people dad?

96

Not while I'm thinking I wouldn't have, not sure people need necessarily have to die Michael I mean, it's probably just a case of, the way I see it we'd be delaying, putting them on hold so to speak, temporarily, suspending them if you like. Getting after them when their backs are turned.

But people might die.

Michael don't be so, he's only messing.

Give it a rest Sinclair.

We shouldn't go killing people dad.

Fair means or fowl son and, if you're going to put it like that then, I don't know, people might die. People might die. People might die at the village fun day mightn't they but that's a risk isn't it, a risk you've got to take I mean, it's not as if you'd go cancelling the fun day just because there was a chance, half the possibility that somebody might go and die at it would you now?

We shouldn't.

Sinclair, please.

How many times, am I talking to myself here I don't know, what do I have to do to be heard in this household, people might die. People might die but, they might not it's not as if, sometimes you've just got to, be prepared to take the consequences.

Dad I'm, I don't think we should.

He's only messing.

Enough of that you.

Really Sinclair, I'm losing my voice here.

Love?

Leave it would you.

Leave what love I'm.

Sinclair please, you're giving me a headache I've had, had about enough of this for one night Sinclair.

I remember Hexalites, remember wanting a pair of Hexalites first day standing on a thorn the Hexalite bursting. I remember only ever being able to serve a tennis ball underarm. I remember either the diameter or the circumference = $2\pi r$ squared. I remember you do not digest tomato seeds, tomato seeds pass unhindered through the human system.

I remember the summer before secondary school going to get a blazer fitted. I remember first day at secondary school the sixth formers big like adult men, being told you'd get a kicking for having your blazer buttoned up. I remember you had to wear a tie being taught to tie a tie. I remember a physics teacher at Ermysted's made most boys cry within the first term of being there, a French teacher with a sweet smell of sweat all around him drank, was said to drink sherry on the job. I remember getting told off for having my shirt untucked, sixteen seventeen being told to tuck it in. I remember Tipp-Ex, writing band names with Tipp-Ex on my schoolbag. I remember Sunday evenings listening to the Top 40. I remember the mnemonic Every Good Boy Deserves Custard, but cannot remember what it might have related to. I remember the acid riff in 'Higher State of Consciousness' remember it was years before I knew to call it acid.

I remember being learnt to smoke, trying not to duckarse Benny Hedgehogs.

I remember sharing headphones back of the bus listening to 'Get in the Ring'.

I remember the Black Widow, the rubber had degraded from being underground but it was still quite the item. I remember I kept it hidden, wrapped in a sock down the back of my bed. Saved up pocket money a few quid's worth of marbles went out to test it, see what it might do. Went out to the edge of the village seeing how far the marbles might go it was hard to judge distance, work out where they landed. I remember wanting something to aim at and aiming at a street light. Edge of the village road up to the moor beyond the last houses. I remember shitting myself when I fluked it, hit the thing. Sound of it smashing, the smell. I guess the smell must have been sulphur, sulphur smell on the air. I remember disposing of the catapult burying it again deeper this time at the edge of a field. I remember being nervous months afterwards if we ever went that way, remember it was a good while seemed like months before the street light got fixed. I remember knocking around sometimes with a lad in the village was scared of the dark would carry a torch with him everywhere he went, fourteen fifteen and always with his torch.

I remember being nervous walking past congregations in bus stops. I remember crossing the road to avoid congregations in bus stops setting off running. I remember shoplifting a chocolate bar maybe a couple of chocolate bars but nothing much beyond that.

I remember a boy in the year above who always had pen on his face, if you mentioned it in the corridor he would get annoyed, say it's not pen it's ink it's not pen it's ink. I remember hiding places, a classroom on stilts, remember I would hide beneath the classroom all through the break times. I remember dad saying not to bother with the set texts saying the syllabus is the silly lie that if I wanted to read something read 'Bobok', if I wanted to read something I should read 'Bobok' instead. I remember when I was doing Shakespeare dad reading him as well. I remember we read *Julius Caesar Twelfth Night*, remember we read *Othello* at much the same time.

I remember Magic Eye pictures you were supposed to go boss-eyed or something, I never once managed it. I remember one day realizing I had underarm hair and being unduly proud of the fact. I remember parched dread, the tension watching *Casualty* until someone got hurt, squash rackets through the neck limbs tangled in machinery, remember an episode once with a manic depressive thought he was a birdman jumped through a glass roof. I remember watching *World's Strongest Man* when an arm got broken during the arm wrestling. I remember the term schizophrenia was coined by a eugenicist. I remember tirrick tern Arctic tern, tirrick tirrick Arctic tern.

I remember you could breathe in breathe out breathe in breathe out into a just empty bottle of pop and if you did it long enough standing up you felt a bit funny light-headed. I remember there was a method of abusing aerosols which involved a t-shirt or clean tea towel which I observed but never practised. I remember venturing into the Red Barn, no stairs, an unfinished building sheep shit on the floor, remember it was a good venue in which to practise smoking. I remember two-toke pass standing in a circle, stringent rules. I remember buckets.

I remember the Birmingham Six remember the Tamworth Two remember a schizophrenic with a machete invaded a primary school picnic in Wolverhampton remember that Peter Sutcliffe was a schizophrenic remember BONKERS BRUNO LOCKED UP. I cannot remember whether Fred whether Rosemary cannot remember whether Dr Shipman was a schizophrenic or not.

I remember loving the double-dotted i in the middle of naïve remember falling in love with the word tundra, an infatuation with the single i in the middle of the word handiwork. I remember thinking ramekin sounded like a made-up word.

I remember being told off, singled out. I remember feeling suffocated scared to speak, punishments deemed degrading, disallowed in the decade or so after leaving that place. I remember if you don't start living in the real world you'll never get anywhere in life. I remember certain teachers wouldn't let me sit near the window.

I remember HELLO BOYS giant boobs in black and white cars crashing at the sight of it. I remember a billboard Kate Moss all covered in foam bubbling suds in suggestive lather in Keighley graffitied SOAPY TITWANK. I remember when Diana died a billboard graffitied CLOTHESHORSE CARKS IT IN FROG TUNNEL. I remember Bingley Music Live was cancelled the next day.

I remember the swimming pool at Ermysted's a tiny little unheated thing boys with blue lips, the games teacher would timetable swimming for February. I remember the cricket pitch the games teacher would make first years bow down to

102

the wicket, remember a sophisticated, multi-year plot to dig the fucker up. We were to leave it a year or two after leaving, dig a trench down the middle of the wicket at two or three in the morning dispose of our tools under cover of darkness. I remember being nervous in music shops afraid to ask questions in case it wasn't cool. I remember sea snakes are the most poisonous snakes. I remember I think I remember there are no poisonous mammals. I remember a day trip once to look at the Humber Bridge. I remember dad telling us that in his youth the River Irwell would change colour as a daily consequence of how the cotton got dyed. I remember car journeys the road up to Widdop burnt-out wrecks in the valley bottom. I remember travelling nthbound on a motorway a car reversing on the sthbound hard shoulder a moment or instance when our motion colluded all motion seemed paused.

It'll be back to black and white if you're not bleeding well careful.

We were only asking.

Not this time Christopher really, I am your father you know.

But it's, everyone else has got one dad.

You'll be asking for a telly in your room next.

Don't be putting ideas in their heads Sinclair.

Lisa's got a telly in her room.

Well that's good for Lisa, isn't it then.

She's had it since primary school.

And whose room would it go in then really, any more of this and we'll be switching back to black and white, keep things certain.

But we, no one's asked for a telly in their room.

Near enough you have.

I was only saying, I wasn't asking for one though.

Be that as it may I, I've had about enough of this. Could you only just think about the world, think about the world outside yourselves for a change?

The world outside myself really dad what do you, I don't know what you mean.

Well just that, for this once could you not be so solipsistic.

Solipsistic?

Yes solipsistic this once, think about the world outside

yourself think about what affect you might be having beyond your boundaries I mean, how many times do I have to tell you, we are not introducing any more magnets into the equation.

Magnets?

Yes magnets how many times do I have to tell you, there's magnets enough in the world as it is.

Magnets I, I'm not so sure you've, what is it, that's so wrong with magnets dad?

What's wrong with magnets? Give me strength.

I'm not so sure I, don't know what you're talking about dad.

Oh come along really, will you not think of the avifauna?

Avifauna?

Yes really, the birds. How are the birds, the whimbrel and the willow warblers going to go about their business if we keep on interfering, putting obstacles in their path?

Obstacles?

Obstacles yes really, am I going to have to spell this out.

It might be a certain help Sinclair, really, what are you getting so het up about?

Well think about it I mean, how do the birds go about migrating when they're at home, away from home I mean, when they want to get to those wintering spots sub-Saharan Africa, the puffins all out in the Atlantic really, it's not as if the geese turn into barnacles not as like the swallows go hiding in millponds is it now.

Barnacles?

Not the barnacles no, the swallows and the house martins, goldcrests on the woodcock and all those throstles, the redwing and the fieldfare on the berries every winter.

We do know what migration is dad.

Well that's a start then see, they're not so sure the scientists quite how the birds migrate, it's not like when they thought the geese turned into barnacles but.

Sinclair they didn't.

Will you only listen for a change I don't know, where do you think the name barnacle goose comes from?

Sinclair?

Why do you think they used to eat them on Fridays really, my own flesh and blood and doubting me indeed but they're past that now aren't they but, they're still not entirely certain but it seems they think, it's more than likely they use the Earth's magnetic field in some way, like there's something in their brains, something about them plugs into, is guided by, guided through the magnetic field and why really, would you want to go interfering with a thing such as that?

But it's only a video player just one dad, they're educational.

It might not be such a bad idea Sinclair.

Am I the only one with any principles left round here, the lot of you. Ganging up, surrounding me again.

Principles Sinclair we are not, it's, can we not have a reasonable discussion in this household. We don't want them getting left out.

How could they, anyone be getting left out when there's a world, whole world outside themselves, world enough to be getting out into.

They're educational dad.

It would be useful for school.

Educational my foot really, I'll give you educational less of this, just the one I don't know, what do you think would happen if everyone, the whole village were to go recording *Neighbours* at once, are you really trying to tell me that all those magnets together at once wouldn't get in the way, that the lapwing wouldn't come down from the moors, start pecking away, interfering in people's gardens, you wouldn't get seabirds, guillemots and razorbills wrecking in from the coast? Could you not, am I the only one round here will think of the lapwing, the green plover, the teewits.

I remember king of the microwave, lord of the rings remember dad cooking chips liver and onions. I remember first time I had a battered Mars Bar I had a headache for the rest of the day. I remember a chippy down the road from school started doing them started battering whatever you liked for 40p it was. I remember all sorts getting battered the whole thing escalating through Toblerones and Milky Ways and packs of Maltesers even, even packs of Maltesers.

I remember that Prince had his lowest, non-essential ribs removed and it seemed a perfectly reasonable thing for a famous person to have done. I worked once with a lad ten years younger who'd heard the same but with Marilyn Manson and we wondered who if anyone the kids nowadays understood to have had non-essential ribs removed. I remember Jet from *Gladiators*.

I remember when Christopher went to university I remember when Helen went to university. I remember after Christopher left swapping rooms moving up, that I went into Helen's and Helen went into Christopher's, remember my old room becoming a study, place to dry clothes. I remember the first term when Helen went to university missing, how much I missed her someone to talk to. I remember there was a payphone on her corridor leaving messages to ring back. Standing in her room actively missing as if missing her was an activity I might actively practise, engage in. Standing in her room hollow like a cave. I remember going to visit Helen at university changing trains at Birmingham. I remember wondering why do you travel on a train but in a car.

I remember *Faces in the Water* first reading Janet Frame not quite, remember I was not quite prepared for all of that. I remember Ken Kesey writing in the sixties saying we should now be witnessing the sunset of ECT. I remember the only Nobel Prize awarded in the field of mental health was something to do with lobotomies. I remember that Sweden kept on with eugenics until into the seventies.

I remember occasional cattle grids with ramps for hedgehogs frogs, so small mammals might climb out. I remember lithium grease is a domestic grease remember under certain circumstances certain quantities of lithium being used to warn coyotes from worrying sheep.

I remember one of the few holidays in France I can remember without Helen or Chris. A municipal campsite, cold dripping showers. Somewhere we hadn't been before such as the Massif Central, although it feels like it was more likely to have been on the coast. There was a cafe nearby and I'm not sure if I would have had a soft drink or was being introduced to responsible drinking. At lunchtime going there to play pool with dad. One day we had a game with a couple of locals who were much better than us and stipulated that you had to finish by doubling the black. They were on it for a long time, something like ten to twenty shots while we trudged our way through the yellows, missing straightforward shots, balls over the pocket. Ten to twenty shots on the black over what must have been a quarter of an hour or more, the cafe getting ready to shut for the afternoon, lights going out on the bar. Somewhat inevitably dad potted our last yellow and first time whammed no hesitation whammed the black off the cushion into the middle of the, the middle of the middle of the pocket. I remember we agreed it was embarrassing, given how much better than us they had been.

I remember when almost anything all things were an embarrassment.

Sinclair really it's a bit, is it not a bit late for this is it really such a good idea?

Love really it's not so late I, I don't know what you're getting at.

It's gone half one Sinclair it's getting on for two though.

The night is young then isn't she just.

Not if you have another cup of coffee she won't be Sinclair.

Have a little faith love, please.

Really Sinclair this is not, isn't a matter of faith will you, you were planning on getting some sleep weren't you and, seriously Sinclair, what good is another cup of coffee going to do us now?

I need to, things need thinking through don't they.

Thinking it through's what we've, you've been doing all night isn't it though and, really, are we any nearer I mean wouldn't trying to, if you were able to get, try and get some sleep I mean, there's work in the morning I do need to function.

Well get yourself to bed love I'm not stopping you.

Sinclair I can hardly, it's not as if I'm going to be able to sleep is it, with the thought of you like this.

Like what love really, there's things need thinking through.

So you keep saying but really we're, seem to be, we just seem to be going through it the same as you have been, don't seem to, it's not as if we're getting anywhere for all your thinking it through.

Well that's what the coffee's good for isn't it though, to stimulate the mind garnish some clarity, insight onto the situation.

What good's clarity Sinclair now though even if it were, even if another coffee were to bring some clarity what could be done, what would you be able to do with it that couldn't wait till morning but, when do you, you're not listening Sinclair.

Are you having one?

If you are then how could I not Sinclair really, this hour, I am not having you by yourself fretting the night away.

There's no need to fuss about it love.

Sinclair it's two, near enough two in the morning don't go telling me I'm making a fuss when it's, all night Sinclair we need, you need to get some sleep I'm, to be leaving the house inside five hours Sinclair.

Well if you are and I don't know, there's no need to be making a dance routine of it is there now.

A dance routine how am I, how do you expect me to, how am I supposed to be doing a halfway decent job when I haven't slept properly in weeks, had so much as a moment's peace.

Well phone in love I'm not stopping you.

Phone in Sinclair really I've a full timetable it's, I've exam classes Sinclair.

One day's not going to hurt them is it love I mean, they can always find cover for one day.

And what am I supposed to tell them this time Sinclair?

Well I don't know but it's up to us, up to you isn't it I mean, they're our rules aren't they now?

Our rules Sinclair, give over will you.

No I mean yes I mean why not, we can decide can't we, it's up to us if we feel like, feel like having a holiday, go calling things a feast day, our word if we want to take the church on pilgrimage.

Listen to yourself I don't know, it'll be both of us out of a job if this carries on.

Why though it's, believe in yourself for a change.

Sinclair please, I can't just be phoning in.

Why not I, I think we, I might be onto something here.

Not again.

Not what love really, hear this one out.

Keep your voice down that's, there's movement upstairs.

I'm only modulating, keeping a course with yours love.

Really Sinclair, at least when we're in the kitchen.

What it's, a man's allowed to speak up in his own kitchen isn't he now?

Sinclair really that's, I can hear creaking on the stairs.

Mum?

Yes Michael?

I woke up and I, I can't get back to sleep mum.

Do you think you might be able to try again for me love?

I could hear talking and, is everything alright?

Yes love it's, everything's ok it's, sorry if we're being loud it, it's got a bit past our bedtime as well.

I'm all awake.

You'll have to, if you could try and get back to sleep. Maybe it's, you can read for a bit if you like.

Can I not sit up with you?

It's a bit late for you to be sitting up Michael I can, I'll get you a glass of water and, reading in bed helps me get back to sleep sometimes.

Thanks mum.

Would you like tucking back in?

I think I'll be ok.

There's a good boy Michael.

Night mum.

Nighty night. Really. If you could at least pretend to keep your voice down Sinclair.

I'm not the only one doing the talking here love.

Sinclair please.

I'm not imagining you am I, I don't know.

Sinclair that's, really Sinclair. This is a touch on the heavy, you've made this a bit thick.

It's to stimulate isn't it though, to help us think this through.

So you keep saying but what though, what is there that's even to be done with it when they have been, what could be done if you were to think it through?

They need to know don't they love, the children.

Not now they don't Sinclair, not at this time of night.

Whoever said anything about now love not now love, not while it's all, before we've got the facts in order even.

Facts Sinclair I'm not sure I'm following this.

No love not facts love no, truth. The truth of the matter.

I think it's about time, high time we went beyond facts and looked to the truth, the truth that stands beyond the facts for a change.

Beyond the, it's a bit late for this Sinclair.

Beyond the facts yes the truth yes, beyond the facts the truth, the truth. The truth is how you choreograph isn't it, draw a map through the facts.

A map Sinclair? This is, please.

It'd be a start wouldn't it though, a something to be getting on with. If we could get them to see that facts and truth aren't interchangeable, uncommon currencies of one another we'd be somewhere wouldn't we, just maybe we'd be onto something.

Please Sinclair you're, there's no need to be getting worked up.

All I'm saying is we need to get things don't we, need to get things straightened out, see through the contours. There's too many aren't there, too many secrets as it is.

Secrets Sinclair really, keep your voice down.

Don't be telling me to, not in this household no, yes, there's too many secrets in this household I don't know, how we ever begin to get things done.

Sinclair they're, children Sinclair it's too early isn't it, can we not keep them young a little while yet.

I'd of thought they're ready love.

Not now Sinclair really, not in the middle of the night.

Well I don't know but, always, we could always have another coffee say.

This one's only, I've hardly had the chance to touch this we need to, you'll be up all night at this rate.

Good to triangulate, to know what's in store isn't it, we don't want any nasty surprises do we but maybe, maybe that's the point isn't it, maybe that's what we've been talking about all along I mean are there though, are we going to have any surprises in store or will it just be, these routines from now on.

Routines Sinclair it's, this is hardly a routine hour is it Sinclair, honestly, keep your voice down. You've woken Michael once already.

Just that it's so, it's predictable isn't it, all this, being here. If we were to go somewhere, up sticks and go somewhere I mean, where you wouldn't know when the sun was coming up, where even to fetch the paper. If we were all to up and run. South America but why is it, why must it always have to be South America when there's a world to get lost in, why not Svalbard or St Helena, Gough Island I don't know, somewhere beyond the horizon for a change?

Where even is Gough Island, honestly now.

Not Gough Island then but, Svalbard maybe, maybe if we were to give Svalbard that bit of a think.

Svalbard Sinclair, what even is there.

You've seabirds haven't you, plenty of geese.

Not geese again.

You do get them.

Probably not what most people would flee the country for.

Since when have we wanted to be most people Caroline?

You're putting words in my mouth Sinclair it's, who even, Svalbard I don't know. There can't be that many can there, places to hide?

Maybe that's, it must be mustn't it though, at least some part of the point. They're always running aren't they, don't want to be getting found, keep running and running. All that jungle I mean, it'd be something, wouldn't it that? To get lost in the jungle, if only for a while and, disappear from it all, turn our backs. The responsibilities the all of it, such bleeding rigmarole.

And whose rigmarole is it Sinclair really, which one of us can't get a seat on the train?

Not this again.

Not, how many times I mean, if you only could.

A little excitement though.

I've had about enough, had it up to my back teeth with excitement Sinclair will you not, think outside your head for a change, follow your own example just once.

Not the jungle then but, if you're going to be like that, it needn't have to be the jungle but, a lighthouse. Why not. Imagine what it would be like for them, to be growing up in a lighthouse. Out there on the rocks of it, in the sea with the rhythm of it, all that, so very much ocean. Waves crashing and crashing. Out there on a rock, our own island even with its, the tideline to wander I mean, would you only go and think about it though. If only for a moment. Out there on our rock and stretching the tideline, walking the tideline to gather some drift it's, that's your word isn't it, drift. Drift yes what is it, the flotsam and the jetsam which is which, there's one's goods overboard isn't it, so much weather, to be out in it on our rock all exposed, looking forward to a touch of warmth, anticipating that. Getting out in the weather to enjoy the warmth of inside, but.

I remember the *Catcher in the Rye*. I remember *Zen and the Art of Motorcycle Maintenance*. I remember not ready, fifteen years old, not really ready getting it out from the library gulping the fucker down, reading till three, four in the morning, daylight. I remember I found it brilliant, brilliant and troubling, the notion of erasure or displacement inherent within. Before/after. The notion that the central character might be two separate characters, that certain treatments/methodologies might in all due respects erase a person, allow them to be usurped, taken out, displaced from within their own bodily substance. The before and after of a man. I remember going to watch the salmon leaping.

I remember rainy days rolling roll-ups in phone boxes shop doorways. I remember putting my head inside a jumper to get roll-ups lit. I remember baggy jeans wider than shoes wet days dragged through puddles soaked up to the knees. I remember a kebab shop Mr Chips in Skipton matters of hygiene remember vague, unsubstantiated rumours graffiti in the pub next door MR CHIPS = COURGETTES. I remember the After Dark in Skipton people called it the After Death the After Birth the Pre-Come instead.

I remember ways of adapting, amending cock-and-balls drawn on exercise books and lever arch files. I remember I did not appreciate olives on first acquaintance. I remember staying up one Monday each year willing Jimmy White on. I remember phone numbers and area codes, remember the phone numbers of people I went to school with, people I haven't spoken to in twenty years, more than that. I remember the millennium bug. I remember thinking Billericay was a place in Northern Ireland. I remember thinking Leighton Buzzard was a character from a Western. I remember peeling onions and thinking you're past the skin only to unveil another layer of pretty-much-skin beneath the, I suppose you might call it the fruit. I remember chewing gum on the underside of desks. I remember chewing gum on the back of bus seats. I remember cock-and-balls converted into rockets cock-and-balls converted into American football players, quarterbacks. I remember bits inside potatoes that looked like caves. I remember triangles have three sides Wednesday is in the middle of the week March is the third month in the calendar, remember blue is a colour green is a colour remember unicorns have four legs circles go round and round stairs go up and down I remember Arctic tern tirrick tern I remember.

Not when the children are supposed to be in school Sinclair, while I'm supposed to be at work. When I haven't had a wink, so much as a wink of sleep.

It was you was saying life's to be about more than the work, about working every day love.

I didn't suggest the kids should be taken out of school.

It's only fair isn't it, if we're to be having a run out.

So you keep saying but, thanks love.

The beauty of it.

Hot yes, that is a, a welcome yes.

If you could only, might bottle that the alchemy of the thing.

Not this again Sinclair not now.

I was only, just making an observation love.

You and your observations Sinclair.

That first taste though, the quench in the mouth and the day outside all breaking open, ready there for the taking.

Let's not be getting greedy about it I don't, the children they, they're supposed to be at school.

If we take what we can. Should be quiet shouldn't it, up on the moors?

It better had be.

Why though, must we be so ashamed?

Sinclair it is not a, a case of being ashamed Sinclair, just. We don't want it do we, being seen.

Why not though, unless we're, be proud of yourself your family this once.

Am I talking to myself again it's, how many times must I, the children. The children are supposed to be at school.

Well let's make the most of it then, while they're not.

We don't want to make too much of it Sinclair.

What love it's, we don't want it, the day to grow cold.

So you keep saying but, can you at least see if they're ready.

Well I've told them to put their coats on, but. Kids!

Dad?

Yes Michael?

Can I take some books with me?

Not this time Michael we, we don't have to be, shouldn't be out so long we thought it would be better to go for a drive this once, catch the weather while we can.

Catch it?

Make the most of things yes at least to, get a bit of a run out and a, a change of scenery at the very least.

Are you about ready love?

I just need to put my shoes on.

Could you give your face a bit of a wash as well please?

Yes mum.

There's a good boy.

Mum?

Yes Helen?

Will we be out all day mum?

Who knows love it's, a day like this all that out there, who knows where we should get to, if we get off to a good, some ample start.

I wouldn't have thought so love.

Don't be so pessimistic it's, with the wind in our sails and all pushing together we could, there's no stopping where we might be ending up.

Could you leave your magazine at home please.

But.

But nothing really, we've told Michael he's to leave his books and if he can cope for a few hours I'm sure you'll be able to manage as well. Everybody ready?

Yes mum.

You've washed your faces?

Yes mum.

Sinclair, are you?

Just checking the oil love.

Dad are we, is the car going to be alright dad?

It'll be fine.

Will it break?

Look I've said it'll be fine now, no fighting in the back, you hear me? We all need to be united this once, falling in the same direction.

Yes dad.

Sinclair.

Love?

Could you open your window a touch Sinclair?

Can we not, wait till she's had a chance to heat up first?

Not if we're going to, if you're going to insist on smoking really Sinclair.

Remind me again which one of us is doing the driving here.

Sinclair really, that's besides the point.

Well if it so happens to be besides the point then maybe you could all just happen to get out and walk for a change.

Sinclair it's, you were the one who decided.

Well a man can change his mind, can't he love.

Really Sinclair, not now.

All I'm, maybe we don't need to make a day of it is all I'm saying.

You know that's not what I meant Sinclair please, could you at least open it when you're done, allow things to dissipate a little.

Whenever do I not and, will you look at that really, isn't it something, to be here now. You see that Christopher?

It's just the sky.

Just the, I don't know. Give me strength the, just the bleeding sky. My giddy aunt. A sky all vaulted like that with the sunlight breaking through and you say it's just the, I don't know if I've the words for some of this. My giddy aunt and me. Helen, you haven't given up on me it's something, you can get some appreciation out of that can't you Helen?

It is pretty dad.

Well there we are then, moving together for a change.

Dad?

Yes Helen?

Where is it, that we're even going dad?

North.

North?

Why not, if we make a, keep up this pace we could really be getting on, towards Svalbard by evening.

Svalbard?

If we get a run of it the wind in our sails, go with the grain of it.

What's Svalbard?

North.

North?

North yes it's, Svalbard's north and that's where we're, with the grain of the compass running true.

Why though?

Because north Michael really, do you need a reason more than that?

Don't be, Sinclair stop it fooling them we are not, only, we're only out for a bit of a drive is all.

Nonsense I'm not fooling, no one's being fooled here if, if we don't allow distractions, all push together this once we could, could be getting on for something today.

Really Sinclair it's, stop it now please. There's distances involved even getting to, even getting to Aberdeen is further afield than you might think. Leave it alone.

Well I didn't say we'd get there did I, I said if we push, only push along we'll be getting somewhere.

Even at a push Sinclair really, at some point we'd have to stop wouldn't we, call it a day. Some of us do need to sleep.

Stays light up there doesn't it love if we only follow the compass you'll feel it, catch yourself some wind again.

Not forever it doesn't and, even if it, I'm not sure it's even that much longer yet.

Well it's, it's a classic bell-shaped curve isn't it and, once the year's gone round the turn. Not that I've ever spent a springtime up there but if we only keep on, run into it.

Are we going on holiday?

Don't be silly Michael how could we, what have we even packed?

How many times am I going to have to tell you about picking on your brother Helen.

But it's, how could we be going on holiday when we haven't even packed anything?

I wasn't asking you to answer back.

Why did you ask a question then?

Not now I mean it young lady not, I don't need this from you as well now but, what was it, your question Michael?

Are we going on holiday?

No it's, your father's just. This isn't, we're only having a bit of a drive is all and, you don't need to be. If you, we keep it between ourselves. You shouldn't, don't need to go telling anybody else, even your friends.

Why must we always be ashamed though?

Because they're supposed to be at school Sinclair.

So you keep telling me but, no. Not this time no. You tell them Michael. You too Helen, Christopher. Don't you go being ashamed telling anybody, your teachers, everyone. You tell them to say it came from me.

Sinclair.

You tell them from me that yes we've been on holiday, yes today's been our day in the sun, that it was us declared it, that we've declared it a festival and we've bloodywell gone and taken it as a festival, our day, it's going to be, from now on it's going to be about us for a change from now on we're going to be the ones call the shots, declare things.

Sinclair the road.

If anybody asks you tell them they can answer to me, that it's, I'm the one that's having the say here, now, very now, that it's down to me now whether or not we're having a holiday and they can, if they don't like, any of your teachers doesn't seem to like it they can bloodywell answer to me, that I've the authority from now on in.

Sinclair your driving really the road, would you please watch the road Sinclair.

Don't be so nervous love.

Nervous Sinclair it's, slow down really, I'm not sure the brakes can handle this.

It's, don't talk silly love.

Sinclair your speed really there's a car coming.

I've seen him love what do you take me for?

Slow down then.

It's not as if there isn't plenty of road for the both of us love.

Then why's he, why did he look at us like that Sinclair?

Like what?

You didn't see the way he looked the way he gestured Sinclair?

Well he can fuck off can't he.

Sinclair.

He can, he can fuck off is what he can fucking well do, gesturing at us.

Sinclair your, your language Sinclair please.

What he can, looking at us funny. Christopher. You're old enough to, you tell him Christopher.

Tell him what dad?

Just, you tell him to fuck off son.

Sinclair.

What he can, he can fuck off is what he can fucking well do and, sometimes. Sometimes you've just got to tell people to fuck off.

Sinclair really, Michael is in the back you know.

To think I wouldn't but, really love I don't, what's the point you're making here love?

Your language Sinclair, honestly, all this swearing.

All what swearing love?

What swearing Sinclair are you, being serious, honestly, if only you could hear yourself Sinclair.

When have you known me not to be serious love really, who's been swearing?

Sinclair.

What have I.

Telling people to fuck off Sinclair.

Since when's fuck off been swearing love I don't know.

Sinclair.

What it's only, but a Saxon word isn't it though.

And we're supposed to be Saxons now are we?

Don't go putting words into my mouth love I, it's all they are isn't it though, all the supposed swear words actually happen to be. They're just Saxon, old Germanic terms for perfectly healthy bodily functions aren't they, rather than the what is it, the Latin or the French say, like shit as opposed to excrement, vagina instead of.

Sinclair.

What?

Really Sinclair, Michael's, the children are in the back you know.

Well so they are but we don't, don't want the children growing up ashamed of their bodies do we now. Give me strength. Up here on the moor with all that, all that moorland in front of us and you're asking the children to be ashamed of themselves really, is that what you want, want them to take from today?

Sinclair really that's, what are you doing Sinclair?

What's it look like I'm, pulling over aren't I love.

What for?

This chap up ahead.

Who?

This chap.

What about him?

To see if he, whether he might not want a lift.

A lift Sinclair I don't know, where is he even going to.

Don't be so, I mean let's be, do something magnanimous for a change and, wind your window down will you.

Really Sinclair.

Set an example love, the children are in the back.

Whoever said they weren't?

We can agree on something then it's, you need a lift there?

Hop in, save your legs. Budge up you three, make some room.

The seat belt's stuck.

Well unstick it then, I don't know. Budge up a bit. Chosen a day for it haven't you, up here on the moors? People say it's, I've heard them say it's bleak don't they but, never understood that myself. Up here with the clouds rolling over, heather coming into life. It's something isn't it, up here with the year on the turn. Could have sworn I heard my first chiffchaff this morning can you, with the windows down you can hear them can't you, the curlew? Back again from the coast. Wouldn't be getting that with a video recorder would you now, wouldn't get that with the magnets, if you'd stayed at home, been playing with your magnets.

Not the, I don't think we need to be hearing about the magnets Sinclair.

Love I'm, a man up here knows to avoid his magnets, don't you though?

Sinclair.

What it's, got to make the most of them don't you just, days like these they aren't here forever. Up here with the clouds rolling over you're not, not here to be checking up on us my wife's looking a bit, not a truant officer come to check on the children are you now? Didn't think as much. You know they say beggars can't be choosers don't they, I've heard them say it myself but if you only, you're not a truant officer are you, not here to be filling in forms, getting out the carbon paper but, if you only look it up, go looking the word up, have a look at your word truant in the dictionary you'll see, it's someone who chooses to beg isn't it, that's the original meaning of the word right there. Someone who chooses to beg you could, religions have been founded on less than that.

Sinclair it's, really please.

Don't be so.

We don't need an etymology lesson Sinclair.

I'm not sure what you mean love it's, all I'm saying. You wouldn't be getting that with your magnets would you, up here with the curlew back again, sound of them calling the curlew, how people think a magnet can give them that, I don't know. Putting faith, trust in magnets when there's all this up here, we don't want the magnets unsettling the compass when we've all this up here, it's.

Sinclair give it a rest. He wants you to stop.

What love it's, you're not, you getting out already are you? Saved your legs a bit haven't we, you've saved yourself a bit of time.

Sinclair really now.

What?

Chatty fella wasn't he.

I've got a numb leg.

Don't be silly your, your leg can't have gone numb so quick.

Michael's been sitting on it.

How else would you have made room. Really, sometimes. I do wonder, if we've been bringing you up quite right. A numb leg, really. You've got to, I do wonder, if you even think of other people sometimes.

It was only down the road dad.

That's just it isn't it though, I mean, it's only down the road and you're in the back there complaining about having a numb leg really now. It's just about, lending, giving somebody else a hand, thinking about the world beyond yourselves for a change, something different. To think of other people but yourselves.

Sinclair.

When you're older I mean now as well but when you're older especially. We don't want, your mother and me the last thing we want is for any of you to grow up and be selfish, not go thinking of others. It doesn't matter, we don't want you to think it matters how much you've got, whether you've, what your shoes are like or whether you live in a big house or any of that crap.

The road Sinclair.

You'd think I'd never driven before love. Your mother and me all we want is you to be happy is all and, not to be selfish, that's the main thing really, that you think of other people, don't go being solipsists about it all. I mean if you were to grow up and find yourself living in the fanciest house, driving the biggest car I don't know, it wouldn't make a blind fig of difference if you were to go keeping it to yourselves.

Sinclair.

I'm not lying am I love?

Well no but, what are you.

Making a cigarette.

When did you start, rolling your own again Sinclair?

I fancied the change is all.

But not, while you're driving Sinclair really, please.

It only takes, doesn't take a minute love.

How long does it take to have a crash Sinclair please, could you not, at least, could you not at least wait until we get on a straight or I don't know, slow down a little Sinclair.

You'd think I'd never driven before.

Really Sinclair.

How else am I to have a smoke round here love?

Can't it wait I mean.

You can tell you've never smoked.

Well I don't know pull over then really, you are not, I am not having you rolling cigarettes at the wheel, not when the children are in the back when there's, corners Sinclair. I shudder to think this is, too much now, please.

There's no need to get hysterical love.

Sinclair I am not getting historical.

Hysterical.

Hysterical yes I know Sinclair yes, hysterical. Hysterical yes Sinclair hysterical.

You said.

I know damn well what I said Sinclair could you, I haven't had so much as a wink of sleep and here I am trying to keep you somewhere away from the red and the children, we've the children in the back slow down, could you please, only, I'm losing my voice here asking you to slow down all the time pull over, could you only pull over Sinclair please.

Calm yourself down love.

Calm me down Sinclair please, I said to pull over.

Look I can't just, can't just pull over can I, I mean do you want us getting stuck in a ditch love I'll, when there's a chance I'll pull over but what is it, why do.

Just to, pull over really so as, you can, so you can roll your cigarette without us fucking well crashing and I can, can only try and breathe a little.

Wind your window down then.

Not like, so we can all just breathe a little and, get out of the car it's all a bit, claustrifying isn't it, being in here all day.

But it's, raining mum.

We'll get soaked.

Look I don't care if there's a bleeding well hurricane out there. Your father's going to pull over and he's going to smoke himself his cigarette and, five minutes, we're all going to have five minutes outside the car before, we go again, keep on driving and, even if it pours even if it buckets it down we're still going to, all going to have five minutes outside the car.

But it's.

What have I just said and, anyway, it's not so bad is it, not raining so much but a little rain, a little rain never hurt anybody did it now.

But, dad's parking in a puddle.

You're not made of soap.

But.

It'll have to be here unless you want me to keep driving.

I said to stop.

And stopping's what I've gone and done but.

We're in a puddle.

Will you only hear yourselves it's not as if we've had forty nights is it now, not like we're asking you to dive into the Great Flood.

I haven't got wellies on.

Well no but, don't let that be stopping you.

We'll get wet feet.

Look just, get yourselves out there I don't know, to hear you you'd be thinking we were asking you to step off a cliff I mean, wet feet. Whoever heard of wet feet being such a problem and, no more excuses stop being so silly now.

But.

This isn't up for discussion.

It's windy.

We are on a moor you know.

I am catching a cold.

Don't be silly Michael not now I mean, really. Five minutes. To clear the air, let your father have his smoke and, make the next ones. Just, five minutes only.

But it's.

Oh enough of that really, listen to your mother.

But.

Really now, if I hear so much as a word more the lot of you'll be going to bed without any supper tonight and, while we're here actually, there's something we've been meaning to tell you.

Not now Sinclair.

It's as good a time as any love.

But while we're, getting some air I mean.

We can't just keep putting it off love.

Are you getting a divorce?

A divorce no what makes you, say that really. Whoever heard of such a thing, me and your, your mother and me getting a divorce I don't know, what could make you say a thing like that?

You've been arguing.

You're always arguing.

No this isn't, we haven't been arguing not really no. It's just that, that we've got a lot of things to talk about because we love each other so much.

Are you going to be having another baby?

Well it's, maybe we will but that's not.

Am I allowed a say in this Sinclair?

Really love it's not so out of the question is it now?

That's easy enough for you to say.

I lost sleep as well love.

Give me strength Sinclair.

I'm not making this up love.

I'm not disputing, saying you didn't Sinclair but, it's hardly giving birth not like you were breastfeeding is it now.

Well no but no one's saying it was but, we can talk about this later I mean, me and your mother, we wanted to talk about, the reason why you're not at school today.

Why we're on holiday?

If you put it like that Michael then, yes. Why we're on holiday, yes. It's, me and your mother when we talk, in the evenings when you've all gone to bed and we talk. There's things we talk about, about you, the three of you and we want you to, to know what they are, the things that we talk about.

Sinclair what are you.

Easy love it's, I've got this. When you're in bed and, before we go up and we're talking it's, not always about you but when it is we, we want you to, to know what they are, the things that we talk about.

Sinclair really you're.

I'm what love?

Could you, get to the point I mean we don't want to be catching our deaths out here do we now.

That's just it though isn't it love, that's the very point we're talking about here. Look if you never listen to me again, if this is the only thing I say that you ever pay attention to then, pay attention really please now, listen. Listen to me here. Me and your mother we just, we want the best for you and it isn't, believe me when I say that it isn't up to us to be deciding what that best might happen to be. Whatever it is you do, however you go about things, just. It's not about, like I said before it's not about having a fancy car or how many shoes you've got, where you go on holiday or staying in elaborate hotels I mean, if there's one thing you take from today take from your mother and me.

Sinclair.

Yes love.

The point Sinclair.

I'm getting there love it's just, honouring life. That's all it's about really, all that we can ask of you. That you should honour life. And that should be, it doesn't mean you have to go running with the bulls or anything like that just, that you honour it, give back more than you take and make the most, do what you can to make the most out of things. Even if it just, if it means simply, just the way you go about things day to day I mean, how you go about your business.

Should we take days off?

Maybe but, perhaps that's not the best example no, maybe not, you shouldn't be taking days off school, we don't want you choosing to beg but, we've taken the day, we've taken it haven't we and me saying this is about trying to, to make the most of it. Really, if you only ever take in one thing I say then really, this. Honour, that you should honour life. Me and your mother we've you, have you don't we, we've honoured life through you but, ourselves, that's not the end of it and in the evenings, when you've gone to bed I mean, when we talk and when we think what's best for you, it's not for us. It's for you to decide but simply, if you do what you can, to honour life only.

Dad are you?

No it's, it's just the wind, no.

It is getting a little fresh Sinclair.

I'm cold.

Have we had five minutes?

I'd say about that why not, yes. Why don't we all get back in the car, out of this wind.

I'm not so ready for driving just yet love.

I wasn't saying we had to get going Sinclair just, to get a bit of shelter I mean, it is a touch bracing up here.

I could do with another cigarette first.

Smoke another cigarette then.

I'll have another and then we can get going.

If that's what you need.

Thanks love.

Be getting on for lunch soon.

You want to eat here?

Good a place as any but, bloody hell Sinclair.

What's up now?

We left them didn't we, left the sandwiches on the side.

Are you sure?

Yes I'm, check the boot but yes, I bloodywell am sure
Sinclair.

It's, not to worry love. They're only sandwiches.

Only sandwiches Sinclair I'm dead on my feet here.

Don't stress yourself it's, not so bad we'll just have to, just
have to have a pub lunch is all.

Pub lunch!

It'll be, not to worry love it'll be fine.

It'll bloodywell have to be fine won't it Sinclair.

Really love it's, no need to worry.

Are we having a meal out?

It looks that way.

Can I have scampi?

No promises Michael I mean, we are some way from the
sea.

Not if we get ahead we're not.

Sinclair don't be, starting this again.

Why not though it's, say yes for a change say yes to life, if we get ahead we could be, getting somewhere near enough.

Sinclair we are not going to the coast.

Suit yourself then love but, it's me that's doing the driving round here.

And don't I know it Sinclair really, could you, I'm struggling to think straight here it's, all night Sinclair, if we could only find a place to eat.

What's it look like I'm, we're setting off aren't we it's, keep your eyes peeled in the back you three, give it a shout if you see anywhere that's looking likely.

I like scampi.

That's good Michael.

If anywhere's even serving Sinclair.

Say yes this, stop being so negative for a change.

Up here though Sinclair are we, even going to find anything for Michael to eat up here. Somewhere with a children's menu.

Well we don't need to, it needn't have to be a pub on the moor love it's, there's, we'll find somewhere if we, could always drop over, down into Keighley if needs be, restart the compass.

And put ourselves on view Sinclair.

If you're so ashamed of us, your family love.

Ashamed Sinclair give me, how many times will you.

Have we done something wrong?

No Michael it's, no one's done anything wrong it's, the road Sinclair.

If you don't want us to be seen together.

How many, strength Sinclair it's, if we only try and find somewhere that bit quieter, the children are supposed to be in school.

Make your mind up.

Sinclair all I'm, this is. We don't want to be putting ourselves on display, inviting, if we could avoid any more trouble before we get ourselves home.

We needn't have to eat.

Not eat Sinclair, I wasn't suggesting.

If you're so ashamed.

Sinclair no one's, I'm just, trying Sinclair. Sinclair I am only trying to keep things under, never said a word about being ashamed, please.

It's what you're thinking though isn't it love.

Sinclair that's, take that back Sinclair.

Take what, if you don't want to be seen with me.

Today though Sinclair when, if we could only find, try and find somewhere that's not so, don't want to be caught in a scene.

They can fuck off can't they.

Sinclair it's, the road Sinclair.

They can fuck off thinking we're not, it's our rules not theirs aren't they, anyone goes, if anyone goes looking at us, whoever it is they can fuck the fucking well off. You heard that you three, if anyone goes looking at us funny you tell them from me they can fuck right off.

Please dad, it's.

141

You're going.

Could you please slow down?

Not you as, you'd think I'd never driven before, think I'd never taken you on holiday.

I'm feeling sick.

I thought you liked the bumps it's, you three ashamed as well it's, I'm not having you three ashamed back there. If we, I thought we were together in all of this. If I ever, you ever let me so much as think you're feeling ashamed it's, I'll come down on you like a ton of, you won't like my answer, I can tell you that for free.

Sinclair really, leave them.

I was only issuing a warning love, this is my cars you know.

No one needs, there's no need to be warning anyone Sinclair really it's, none of you have done anything wrong, don't worry. It's just, we're all a little hungry, aren't we all? Could all do with having a little something to eat. It's, don't worry we, we'll find somewhere soon enough.

I'm feeling sick mum.

Oh no don't you ever, don't you ever be letting, even think of letting anyone, any of those bastards your teachers the doctors be saying they're better than you. It's, you show them. From now on I want you to be showing them. You show them it came from me.

Sinclair, please.

What love why must they, is that what you want from them, to be feeling ashamed? On a day like this and all of us together, you don't want them to facilitate them bastards, allow those wastes of skin to be feeling they're better.

Sinclair this is.

I'm not wrong am I love?

No Sinclair I'm not saying but, your language Sinclair the corners. How many times before you listen, how many times do I have to ask about your fucking language before you, when have you ever listened Sinclair when have you ever thought about me it's, this is, please, the corners Sinclair the road. At least on the, when the children are in the back.

It was you was saying you're hungry love.

I didn't say I wanted to have eaten my last supper Sinclair really, you'll get us stopped, must we, how many times am I wasting my breath it's. This is. When do you, have you ever thought Sinclair, Sinclair the

PART TWO

1

I remember being told, dad telling us stories about Grandpa Lancashire, how he learnt to drive, the time he walked over the tops to Burnley to avoid a family occasion. I remember Deerplay Moor, the source of the Irwell. I remember Soil Hill. I remember Grandpa Lancashire went to work at twelve, that he would go to the mill in the mornings, get changed and go to school in the afternoons, that the teachers wouldn't wake those who'd been working when they fell asleep at their desks. I remember being told often, ever so often being told about some kid who would take a stick of chalk out whenever he left the house. Drawing a line in the morning to walk home later. Before the wars the tumult, at a time when chalk wouldn't have come easy. Over the cobbles and I am glad no one is asking me to explain my reasoning, but everything in my head is black and white, gradations of grey save for the chalk scratched blank as a migraine, an absence of colour etched into a tightrope. I see it now, can still picture it spreading, drawn in the morning and redrawn as it was later traced, the line followed homeward, flowing out from itself throughout the eddies and fluctuations of a hand not entirely steady. I can still picture the word palimpsest scrawled atop an East Lancashire cotton town. How thick it might have become if followed for three, four days, a week without rain. What might have occurred in time of drought, mill waters running dry.

I remember West Yorkshire's answer to the Taj Mahal, some house near Todmorden built for the love of a woman who chose against it, moved to Switzerland instead. I remember there was a breed of fighting cock called the Keighley Grey, that there was a donkey from Keighley that lived to ninety-four. I remember there were times when dried frogs might be worn in a pouch round the neck as a cure for headaches and melancholy. I remember there was a chap from Keighley who did not leave his room did not leave his bed, that he stayed under the covers for forty-nine years, that he stayed under the covers so long as to become an object of national curiosity, some unwitting tourist attraction. I remember vacancy, moments of vacancy, that I would filter out, grow distant from situations not know what was going on, in a German lesson once not understanding that I had been asked a question, failing to comprehend that I had even been asked a question. I remember nur ein bisschen Deutsch. I remember Bedeutung. I remember making a contraption, gathering wood and assembling a frame so dad could go about the swapping of the engines. I remember the problem was words, that people used words they didn't know the meaning of, used words that didn't mean the first bit of sense to begin with. I remember the police coming the first time I can remember the police coming to take him away I thought, being told or thinking, thinking that they had taken him away on holiday somewhere, that they had taken him to go and stay in a hotel. I remember when we threw the electricity out of the house.

Just because your father never puts anything away doesn't mean it's a habit you're to be getting into.

I don't see why it's me has to dry.

Someone's got to.

Yeah Helen.

I did it yesterday as well.

Well that's, you'll have to get on the washing-up next time really, you are all a help.

But Michael isn't even doing anything.

Michael laid the table didn't he, it's.

Laying the table's not doing anything though.

You can lay the table tomorrow Helen I don't know, do you want me to draw a rota up let's stop, there's no need to start being silly about it. Talking won't get things put away any faster.

But he never does anything.

I laid the table.

Just because he's the youngest.

What have I just said.

I'm doing it.

You are a help but, what are you ferreting about in there for Michael?

A pair of scissors.

Scissors?

I'm only getting a pair of scissors.

Not from in there Michael.

Why not though?

Because it's, they're kitchen scissors how many times.

But what else, am I going to cut things small with?

We do have other scissors you know, they're not for paper.

But I don't know where they are.

Have you checked your pencil case?

I don't know where it is.

Have you thought about having a look?

Not yet.

Really now, you're getting as bad as your, if you could at
least have a look for it, save us some of this kerfuffle.

But I don't know where it's got to.

Well that's what looking's for, isn't it just.

But.

Stop being so selfish Michael.

I am not being selfish.

Helen really, go easy on your brother.

I only want to make a couple of cuts.

Not with the kitchen scissors Michael, we've only just
got them it's, have you thought of looking under your bed,
checking the windowsill, there's no need to do anything
drastic just yet.

I remember molten cheese, biting into too hot pizza the roof of the mouth peeling, four maybe five days in recovery even. I remember that when Robbie left Take That it was a significant item on the evening news. I remember when the prime minister stuck his oar into *Coronation Street* showed his credentials. I remember wondering if it might not be the molten cheese but the tomatoes, remember is it true that garlic used to come with a health warning, that garlic was kept in the foreign food section of the supermarket. I remember that hot food cooked through is legally required to be ten degrees hotter in Scotland than England and Wales.

I remember that certain countries require more than five portions of fruit and/or veg a day, certain cultures where mirrors and paintings were covered in times of mourning to prevent the new dead from getting distracted as they passed overboard. I never remember looking a gift horse in the mouth. I remember Blur vs Oasis. I remember the Dutch do not have a word for mind.

I remember reading up, research that went nowhere, each cotton mill in nineteenth-century Lancashire having its own signed language for communication over the looms, some chap who taught himself foreign languages amongst so much noise, practised Gothic lettering in the dust, a period when there were so many pubs in the Borough of Rossendale that an ale tester was employed to assess the purity of the drink, that it was said that it was not the length of the road but its width that caused his trouble. I remember that the ale tester attempted to retire but there was no one within the district with so efficient a constitution as might be able to replace his own. I remember that it would get so windy on St Kilda that certain gales might render the entire archipelago temporarily deaf, that they developed their own signed language to cope with such occasions. I remember an East Lancashire solution to the problem of deafness involved boiling the piss of a boar cat.

I remember the nitrogen cycle, I remember oxbow lakes. I remember having to do a geography project on that bit of the beck that separated our garden from the Clough. I remember struggling to get my head around mass-produced garden peas. I remember jigsaws missing pieces visiting time the hours meant getting a bus to the hospital after school. Still in my school shoes, footsteps, echo in the corridors echo within a man, like visiting an echo but smaller, reversed, if that makes sense to say. Visiting an echo but smaller the other way round, swallowed in on itself. Something numbed, smaller about him. Things ashen and missing. Taken. In the summer, if it was still light then we would walk home, forty or so minutes if taking the back way, avoiding the roads. It was built, they said the hospital had been built in error, a miracle of planning permission, that built on a floodplain the whole thing was sinking, foundations ever having to be amended against the inevitability of subsidence.

You never help me with my homework.

Oh don't be, it's not homework just a bit of fun.

Christopher really, thanks for doing the dishes, you don't need me, are more than clever enough to be doing your homework without my helping you.

You're helping Michael.

What have I gone and said, it's not homework Christopher really. A game isn't it, that bit of fun for us to be getting on with. You can join in if you like.

I'm alright.

Well don't say we didn't offer.

I won't.

There you go then, the matchstick. If we were to go about making the matchstick that little bit smaller.

Can I have a biscuit?

You and your hollow legs Christopher.

It's only a biscuit.

Look I'm, I didn't find time to make a pudding, I'm sorry love. We need them for packed lunches there's fruit isn't there, the bananas are about turning.

But dad always.

Well that's as, I don't know. I'm sorry love. You can always help yourself to fruit.

Bananas are a type of herb.

Michael they are not.

They are I, I read it in a book.

No you didn't.

I did Christopher really I did it's, why won't you ever believe me?

Show us then.

It's I got it from the library, I've taken it back.

Whatever Michael.

Helen really, go steady on your brother, it's. A herb I don't know, bananas are a type of herb now.

Can I watch the telly?

If you like but, not for too long and, thanks again for the washing-up.

It's alright.

You are a good help, now. There's still quite a bit of space, isn't there. If we're careful, be methodical about things we should be able to get close to a, be able to get near to a hundred I'd have thought.

A hundred!

If we keep on, don't lose our focus about it.

We're going to be the best.

I'm not making any guarantees just yet.

Going to beat the rest.

No promises but, it is fun, isn't it? We're having that bit of fun doing it and that's what matters, matters more than if, whether we do happen to win or not really, thanks for doing the drying Helen.

I don't mind.

Really love it's, thank you.

It's Michael's turn tomorrow.

And Michael can, will take his turn when it comes.

I like the drying.

Michael stop it, if you like the drying so much why don't you, you can do it every night can't you then.

But I laid the table.

Since when's laying the table been doing anything.

Play nicely you two, if we could all just get along, enjoy a little peace while it lasts.

Sorry mum.

I'm sorry.

There's no good saying you're sorry if you're going to be at each other's throats inside five minutes, I don't know. Why don't, are you going to join your brother?

Maybe I've, some homework to be doing.

You and your homework don't be, spending all night on it love. You've still to find time to relax.

I won't do.

Is that a promise?

I promise.

You really are a help now, where haven't we. The cupboard under the sink if they ask, anyone asks say it was your idea, that you asked and it was me that got things out for you, you are not to be going under the sink without me, detergent.

I remember the blue whale isn't the only animal bigger than a double-decker remember the lion's mane jellyfish is bigger, longer at least than a double-decker bus. I remember waking sometimes in the night thinking what am I, am I animal, vegetable or mineral? What is this substance that forms me, this substance from which I am formed? I remember my shyness counteracting my shyness by going over the top drinking too quick. I remember the future seeming a confined space, closing in.

I remember one time when I would have been at primary school and he was in the hospital. In some way related to a bring-and-buy sale or *Blue Peter* appeal there was a competition, to see who could fit the most items into a standard-sized matchbox. They were handed out in class and we took them home, wrote down the contents on a piece of paper which might have been folded up and held against the box by an elastic band, I'm not entirely sure. I remember struggling to get going and mum saying no, I shouldn't help out, mum saying go on then, everyone else's parents will lend a helping hand. I remember we included a grain of rice and a grain of salt, a grain of sugar and a pepper granule. Examples of white and self-raising and wholemeal flour. A red lentil and a petal from a daisy. I remember mum discussing the issue of air. While it was a given that the constituent parts were to be included, that carbon dioxide and oxygen and probably also nitrogen would be on most people's lists, she wasn't sure whether to include argon, how obvious a sign of assistance that might prove to be. Whether to go smaller than the proton and electron when including features of the atom. What if it wound up a draw, we were to lose by a single item? I remember removing something like a marble or a feather because it was taking up too much space, my role within proceedings becoming more and more remote until I think I abandoned the pretence of even writing out the list, remember that we managed to get over one hundred and thirty items into the box, ran out winning by a three-figure margin.

I remember first going to university living in a city I missed the moor the Clough as much as anything. I remember coming home I would walk up the Clough soon as seeing my mates. I remember always cooking too much pasta it took a long time to understand, to begin to understand how to cook rice. I remember why don't pizza and garlic bread cook at the same temperature for the same precise time. I remember calling the green card in a packet of Rizlas the fillet of roach. I remember blowbacks. I remember Chinese bifters. I remember, in a taxi, thinking I would be able to contain the sick in my mouth and swallow it back.

I remember thinking where did one thing end the other begin, how much was personality was character, where was it the illness the medications, when did the treatments come into play.

I sort of remember Trio bars, remember working with a lad once said he'd been boycotting chocolate in all its forms since Trio bars went out of production. I remember he was nervous about dark foods we had to assure him the fruitcake wasn't some dirty trick. I remember the first time I had a job that summer after school working through a temping agency getting paid by the hour, I would work out how much I earned each week for going to the toilet, would work out how much I earned each week for taking a piss. I remember working with a Czech bloke called Pafka the manager struggled with pronunciation called him Paul instead. I remember a day's work with a builder who said we'd better leave it, let the dust settle. I remember talking about Kafka with Pafka when we were peeling spuds. I remember a bread knife is an important tool when fitting a lawn.

That's, Michael you are being selfish.

Can I not have another five minutes?

Seriously, we'll miss the bus Michael. Stop being so selfish for a change.

But it's, I'll be able to see if it's coming.

Not if you're kicking a ball or up a tree you won't, really, we don't want to miss it.

I'm coming.

Hurry up then.

I've said I'm coming, it's.

Saying doesn't mean a thing if you're not going to go and do it.

The bus is always late isn't it though.

That doesn't mean it won't be on time tonight does it Michael, when did you start being so selfish. You used to be so nice when you were little.

I am not being selfish.

Tell that to dad when we've missed the bus it's, where are you going now?

I just want to have a play on the railings.

You'll make us miss it.

No I won't it's, I can climb over, I've done it loads.

And get stuck Michael really.

It's only the railings Helen.

Not if you get a spike through your leg it won't be.

I can climb over.

Not when mum put me in charge you can't.

But it's easy though.

I don't want to have to explain to her it's, she wouldn't let me let you.

Only until we can see the bus.

I am not letting you climb over.

I can run to the gate though.

I am not getting, asking the driver to wait, having you embarrassing me.

But I'm quick at running.

Not as quick as a bus you're not.

I just want to play a bit longer.

Stop messing.

It's only the railings.

Michael really, I can see it now.

I remember the cream always rises, Grandpa Lancashire sitting the three of us down, saying the cream always rises to the top. I remember Viennettas aren't even that pricey, why were they such a treat. I remember Global Hypercolor t-shirts, t-shirts that changed colour according to body heat showed off where you'd been sweating. I remember twenty pounds was too much to be spending on a t-shirt, a period in my early twenties where it seemed every six months I would meet someone else would say it was their plan to bring back Global Hypercolor t-shirts get rich. I remember a shift once in a sandwich factory, I walked out in the first break. I remember cheap rent, living in a shared house where no one touched the cleaning, when I got round to the bathroom the mat had begun to decompose, to anticipate the moistening scent of leaves as they make their way to soil. I remember almost gipping at bad milk in the fridge. I remember thinking it was me had been curdled.

I remember a tribe in the Amazon with a system of counting that went one, two, three, many, all numbers larger than three grouped in the same amorphous category. I remember thinking there are many glasses in a bottle of wine, that this was how it worked when it came to counting glasses of wine, pints of beer, that after three you were in for the haul, in with the many. I remember a day once when I was paid to watch a skip.

I remember small victories, boiling the exact amount of water for a cup of tea. I remember days when doing the crossword felt achievement enough. I remember greedy boards.

I remember years when I only read Hermann Hesse. I remember thinking Milan Kundera the world's greatest writer. I remember making a meal of the rivalry between Dostoyevsky and Tolstoy, thinking it remained an either/or issue, that because I loved *Crime and Punishment* loved *Notes from Underground* there would be nothing in it for me, I would never get anything from *Anna Karenina*. I remember being in a charity bookshop when some fella walked in, took half a look at the classics said no, I've read them all, goodbye. I remember books yellow and stumbling, the final act of reading a book as it comes apart, the spine falling to powder in the hands. I remember books gone mouldy, irredeemable in damp rooms, remember green mould from spent oranges overtaking a book once left in the bottom of a bag. I remember seeing a chap once, seven in the morning reading *The Man Without Qualities* on the way into work. I remember thinking I needed to up my game. I remember books bought but never read.

I remember making a pig's ear of it.

I remember thinking why do people say teared up rather than tore. I remember bawling my eyes out.

I remember heatstroke. I remember watching a thundercloud all wrapped up in itself, a darkened swelter above the north of the city that convulsed with lightning which never broke through its walls, exceeded such ambit. I remember windchill factor. I remember landslips. I remember everything everything

162

the acid line from 'Rez/Cowgirl' the hairs on the back of my neck. I remember coming to the conclusion that my CDs were all scratched unsustainable, that my CDs were scratched beyond listening, might as well be thrown out. I remember what's another word for pirate treasure. I remember the Magnum point four-four is the most powerful handgun in the world, it will blow your head clean off. I remember going it must have been years eighteen till early twenties without a belt using my school tie instead. I remember that buying and wearing a belt was an important gateway towards smartness. I remember there is a material difference between the imperial and American billion. I remember falling asleep in my clothes to save time come the morning.

I remember a tree that grew like a metaphor in the back garden. Overhung, in the shadow of vast pines, the trunk went every which way, horizontal and downwards as it torqued and curved, stretched its way towards light. I remember smoking carriages on trains. I remember one maybe two occasions smoking in toilets subsequent to the smoking ban. I remember one year a red admiral overwintering in my bedroom. I remember camping up the Clough pitching the tent in the dark forgetting the groundsheet. I remember going to pick at a toenail but causing mischief to the flesh instead.

2

So, here we are. Another year and back here already, arguing again about a tree. Whether it is a good idea to be holding Christmas at all this time, it might not be better to go and call the whole thing off. If there is anything this year to be celebrating at all.

We did not make it to the Pyrenees, did not manage to go camping even the once this year. Without a vehicle the tents alone too heavy, a bit much for myself and the children to bear. Still of course you want to do something, and I managed to get the three of them away, if only for a week. The most/best part of a week walking between youth hostels in the Yorkshire Dales. Limestone territory. Something different for the change. They enjoyed hearing about how it had been when I was their age, only dormitories in which to sleep and dependent on the warden they might not so much as bother with the heating.

Cycling between long-shut hostels in Wales, names I can barely now remember, never could (quite) pronounce. Chores to fulfil as to keep the pennies down. They have changed a bit with cars allowed, but this way still you don't need so much, and they carried their rucksacks without complaint or fuss. We had a family room the four of us together in Ingleton, did a walk counting waterfalls and visited a cave system which was worth the money. Stalactites/stalagmites. From there on to Malham with rock climbers on the Cove and the limestone pavement, which ~~I don't know where they get these things~~, they all insisted on *calling (it) the sidewalk. They did not have a room for the four of us so we slept in separate dorms, myself on the bottom bunk for the first time since before I met him, Christopher and Michael in with a group of cyclists who were using the hostel as a base. We did the Janet's Foss/ Gordale Scar walk and carried on to the tarn, were fortunate that the steps up through the gorge were not too slippery. Lucky overall with the weather. Just a few days but something anyway, ~~slight changing of the scene~~. I gave the children some extra spending money and they used the most of it on gifts for him. Kendal Mint Cake and buttered fudge, emblazoned pencils.*

Sinclair.

Sinclair, Sinclair.

In certain ways it was my first day at work. First real day of what we might call employment, my first day in my first teaching post. He was new at the school and we started talking and that was how it started, the two of us in the staffroom talking together. Neither of us asking so much of the other, when it came to it. Just, that feeling. We both wanted children and as we both wanted children we thought we might as well get married. Our decision so simple as that. That we wanted to be, it would be the both of us from then on after. They wanted to tell him all of it, how far we walked and where we stopped for sandwiches, where they stopped so as they might skim stones. Which hostel did the best flapjack. The rest of the summer for them, I don't know. We took day trips, made use of the buses.

Because of where we are at the edge of a council area you have to get to the boundary first, but after that day passes and family tickets work out well. A bus/rail combined makes going into Bradford simple enough. The media museum is very good, and they all find the IMAX quite exciting. Until recently it was the largest screen in Yorkshire, maybe even Europe? A mean old scene! The village itself is more of the same but I don't know, the bakery has recently been put up for sale and once again it looks as if it will be turned into housing. There is the need of course, but only last week the butcher was saying how much harder the competing is getting, that he can't imagine he'll find anyone to take it over when he does come to calling things a day. If only there were more facilities not less going in with it all, something looked like being done about the capacity in the schools. There was a fire at the chip shop which meant that it was closed for a good few months. It is not as if there aren't others, but it is nice to have one in easy distance.

From where we are you can walk quite well. It is not so far to evoke the moors and we have the Clough on the back doorstep. Christopher has been keeping a record of plants and birdlife, sketching foliage. Dog's mercury, which is a sign of ancient woodland. He is doing the three sciences at GCSE and we like to think that he might perhaps like to work in conservation. Something out in the air. Helen is diligent, keeps her head down. Without having so much as begun her GCSEs she seems quite set upon university. We do wonder if she might be better suited elsewhere, but it would be a lot to have to manage at this stage. Whether another upheaval would be worth it, do so much harm as good. Michael really did enjoy youth-hostelling, went so far as to give a talk in front of his class. They all of them do mostly get along, and it is nice to see it when Helen and Christopher play well with their little brother. Resilience in the three of them. My family as matryoshka set.

Visiting ~~on school nights (cutting short playing in the park)~~, visiting ~~on school nights (still with their homework to be done). Better for (the) all of us~~ to have him back. ~~Funny really that that is not, no place for~~

~~getting well as such, no place at all for being well. (It is) not what I would have, without all this (these years, such years) would I have thought to think as that? That that is not a place at all, not really for the getting well. Safety maybe, you could say it is maybe for/about the safety. If even it is for the stability, I am no longer sure. For them in there it seems to be about the management, getting with the levels, about getting the levels where they can manage them/can manage him, helping with the sleep. Not stability, but. Two hours. Two hours at most a night. The months of that. Him not sleeping and me up all night without him sleeping. Those months of that, this year.~~ Is there anything more that might be said? ~~What we did at the weekend, a talk in front of the class. This year the wiser.~~ One day (maybe) we'll be the wiser for it.

But here now these arguments about a tree, whether there is anything this year to be celebrated at all, worth decorating. Each year the rigmarole of getting it straight, just about getting the thing straight for it to slump again within the day.

What is it that they have to say, the poets? What is it that Wallace Stevens might tell me now? Wallace Stevens says that after the lot, the last fucking breath, that after the final no will come a yes, that it is on such a yes that any future, all permissible worlds must come to depend. The yes itself all present sun. If it were so easy, so easy as that Wallace Stevens I do not know. Really, I do not know. Where even to begin.

The children spent the best part of their money on gifts for him, wanted to tell him all of it, how there was a choice between macaroni cheese and cottage pie at Ingleton, who was best at skimming stones. How far we walked, how long those days of walking took. ~~He was annoyed we hadn't been to visit, such resentment for taking them away at all. Just a few days (not even a week) but the resent of that. Him~~

~~stuck there.~~ *They did well, really, with it. I think that they did well. Months after school each day, one or two or the three of them going to visit most every day. Fitting in with the hours. Michael took in artwork, paintings from school so as Sinclair might decorate, bring colour to his room. His memory now ~~affected~~ afflicted by it all, he can no longer read novels/follow plots. Poetry remains for him, though (even) that at times a struggle. He said it took all day, that some days it took more than the all of the day for him to read, get through a single poem while he was there. Such consumption of his woes.*

The rest of the summer we took day trips, made use of the buses. The Piece Hall in Halifax, which really is quite something/might perhaps be better known. Carlisle on the train. Not that you can see so much of the viaduct when you are going over the viaduct, but still it is a nice journey. They have done well, I think, the children. I think that they do well. From where we were, might have been. Michael when he was young and tired rhyming, all in a muddle and uttering chains of sound, not quite words linked together through rhyme, concatenated. Chicka wicka licka picka. Mooley pooley ooley fooley. When Helen started talking Helen talking and talking. Christopher at three, having memorized most all of the bird book. Three years old and getting the red-backed shrike, the black-tailed godwit right.

The village, I don't know about the village. Four years already, I do not know. The goalposts in the park keep getting broken, they say it is a no-go area after dark. ~~Yobbos putting street lights out.~~ Twitching curtains, who to trust. News lately that the baker's is to be closing and there's supermarkets of course, but the bread is not the same. Only the other week the butcher was saying how much harder it keeps on getting, competing with it all. Says he can't see anyone taking it on as a butcher's when he's done, that near enough and it'll hardly be worth it. Still, what would he do all day, without the routine? Don't suppose it is only here, but you notice it worst/the more when it's in your village. There are people say the park is a no-go area, I don't know. Would be easier if it were on a train line, but overall it's not so bad.

~~Piles of it, the washing-up when I come home.~~

If only I knew what he does all day but he is here now, it is for the better. The doctors there, I don't know, Sinclair says they don't understand the first thing about heads. That if they can't begin to understand the first thing about poetry then however might they understand heads. ~~If only they could learn some little of that, thought better than to put electricity through a brain.~~ If I had not seen, had not been there/these years what would I have thought? Up and out to work to see him, come home, put dinner on the table, eat and sleep and out to work to see him, come home, put dinner on the table. Sandwiches to be made. Without all that would I have thought it was a place for getting better, some place at all for being well? Without all that, these years so wiser, would I have even, ever thought to think at all?

If it were, could be a case of the straight line only, looking back from day to day to see things better from day by day, but. Not that there's, you don't have your moments. One big moment this bleeding year, what to say. Him in there and quoting his own poetry, unwilling to talk to the doctors when they can't grasp metaphors, what is there that might be said? What we did at the weekend, a talk in front of the class. Love. That I loved him and wanted to be with him, go places with him, wanted us to be together in those places that we went. Such feelings as those, the memory of them. As if a memory of such feelings might be retained without being able to recollect quite what such feelings were

170

like. Twenty-six years old, alone in the house. My husband elsewhere, under section. That it is still love is not a lot to say, it is not a lot to say that it has always been love but different, another type, how many types through time, I wonder, if we should, should we say that love is just the one thing because it is just the one word, do we need to say these things as love for them to be known as loving? I don't know. Pregnant with Helen, Christopher not yet two. Sinclair having an episode, Sinclair under section. Those things we have been through. These many times. In the winter rains hearing rocks dragged and smashing together, even with the windows shut the audible turn of the beck as it cuts into the garden. Those moments when you might want to. Say enough. Give in, curl away from it all. Because you cannot, can you, cannot throw your hands up, simply throw your hands up, say not again.

3

No I was not, no.

Michael you were, you were whispering in their, you do know cacti don't have ears don't you?

Of course I, I wasn't talking to them you're making it up.

I've caught you red-handed.

But I'm going to miss them.

Helen, Helen have you heard this, Michael's been talking to his cacti says he's going to miss them, that he wants to take them with us.

I didn't.

You do though don't you, you.

I never.

You do know they're not going to need watering don't you?

Of course I, they're from the desert. You can get, it can go years and years without raining in some parts of the desert.

Why do you want to take them with us then?

I didn't say I did.

But you do though don't you?

I.

Michael admit it.

Go on.

Really, you three, what are you squabbling about now?

It's Michael he, go on Michael tell mum yourself.

That's enough really, how many times do I need to tell you, to leave your little brother at home.

Is he not coming with us?

Alone really, you're getting as bad as your father sometimes just, leave your brother alone for once.

But he's, he was talking to his cacti and he, he wants to take them on holiday.

Oh I don't know about that Michael how would we, fit them all in though.

I could hold onto them.

You've got quite a few you know love.

Just, my favourites. I could hold onto my favourites.

All that way?

All the way yes.

Really Michael your hands'll be tired out before we're through Colne, they don't need watering, will be fine. It's nothing to worry about if we leave them here.

But I don't want to miss it.

Miss what Michael really, they're not going to change so much it's, we're not going to be away all that long you know.

But it's, all holiday.

And all holiday isn't so long Michael but, I don't know, what do you think's going to happen to them in four and a half, five weeks' time?

What if they, I don't want to miss it if they flower.

Oh I shouldn't think, it's not something to worry yourself about too much love really, I wouldn't have thought it's so likely.

But I've always wanted to see them flower.

Really Michael it's, you'll have forgotten what a cactus even is by the time we're back.

They're my favourite thing.

Well, yes.

Desert, the original meaning of desert is an empty or abandoned place.

Is that so?

The largest of all the deserts is the Sahara which is, it's about as large as America, the all of America. There's a type of ant, a silver type of ant that, because it's so hot there the silver ants only leave their nests for ten minutes each day.

You have been reading up.

In the Gobi, Gobi means cauliflower and.

I wouldn't be so sure about that.

It does it means cauliflower and, the desert is the.

The cauliflower desert Michael?

What have I just said, about leaving your brother alone?

But mum, you can hear him he's, the cauliflower desert mum.

It does though, Gobi means cauliflower and in the desert.

The cauliflower desert?

Will you two stop that please.

But mum he, Michael keeps calling it that mum, you can hear, it's him keeps calling it the cauliflower desert mum.

Not in so many words he doesn't and, how many times must I have to remind you, your brother is younger than you, cut him some slack.

But, the cauliflower desert mum.

Yes yes, the cauliflower desert yes but, what was it Michael, you were going to say, about the caulifl, the Gobi Desert I mean?

It's a, the Gobi Desert is a windy desert.

A windy cauliflower desert?

That's enough Christopher really, let your brother speak for a change.

It's a, it's really windy, one of the windiest places on Earth and because it's so windy it's not sandy like you might think a desert normally is, there's not so many sand dunes because the wind, the wind only goes and blows it all away.

That's nice Michael.

The wind blows the sand away so it's rock, the ground. The ground is nothing but rock and, there's no water only rock.

Where do all the cauliflowers grow then?

Helen really, you should be encouraging your brother. Carry on Michael.

It's, I'm not sure why but it's one of the best places for dinosaur fossils and there's even, I think there's even dinosaur eggs in there, that if you're lucky you might find dinosaur eggs in it.

I didn't think you were interested in dinosaurs so much any more?

I'm not but, only when, if you get them in the desert.

That's good to know.

There's actually, one of the reasons why deserts are so interesting is that things do live in them and lots of things do actually live in the Gobi Desert.

In spite of the wind?

Even though it's so windy yes. There's a type of fox and a sheep I think and a camel, a kind of camel you don't get anywhere else.

Is it a dromedary?

No it's a, they call them Bactrian camels and you don't get them anywhere else. There's a type of sparrow and antelopes as well, I don't remember what they're called but there's special antelopes and you only get them in the Gobi they've, they've got, need funny noses in order to live there.

Funny noses?

They look a bit like they've got a cold, might be all bunged up.

Maybe they could do with some decongestant.

I don't think it's, I think it might be dangerous, if you were ever to go to the Gobi Desert.

Would it?

I think so.

Is that because it's a, because deserts are dangerous places?

Not just, I don't think it's only that no.

Isn't it?

I don't think so there's things there, that live under the ground.

Underground things?

They're very long and they burrow.

In the rock?

In the, because they're very dangerous yes, they can be, they're between two and five foot long and the people, the desert people are scared of them because they're so dangerous, they're so dangerous that they call them death worms.

Death worms?

The Gobi death worm.

Really, well, the Gobi death worm indeed I, I can't say I've ever heard of such a thing.

They can be anything up to five feet long and they spew acid if you get too near them but it's worse than that because even at a distance, even at a great distance they can kill.

Can they now?

They can. They can kill at distances because they shoot out electricity, expel it through the air.

Michael really, you can't believe this.

Christopher.

But, have you heard him mum seriously it's, whoever even heard of a death worm mum?

I've read it though it's, it's in the book.

So should we believe anything now, just because it says so in a stupid book?

Christopher please.

I read it in the book and, they spew acid and can be up to five feet long, they're dark red like clotting blood and so poisonous that even if you were to touch a dead one it would kill you even then.

Michael that's, do you believe in fairies as well now Michael?

Fairies no I never, didn't say anything about believing in fairies.

What about Nessie?

Have you gone and started believing in Nessie again?

But there's photos.

Photos Michael really, it's a bleeding stick.

Language Christopher how many times do I have to tell you really, your brother's only nine.

I'm almost ten.

But have you heard him mum, seriously.

Just, don't forget that you're older Christopher and anyway, it can be fun can't it sometimes, to believe in things.

But, mum.

What would dad say, if he heard him talking like this?

Your father's in bed Christopher, allow him his beauty sleep.

Beauty sleep?

Let him get his rest.

I wasn't saying to wake him.

There's photos.

It's a stick.

Not for sure it's not.

Michael, honestly, you'll believe anything if you read it in a book.

I remember when Christopher left when Helen left feeling so, that I was so alone with it all no one to talk to might understand, who understood what it meant to not to understand. I remember deep waters wanting to stand in deep waters remember curiosity a certain itch, wanting to know what was round the corner, round the corner beyond the corner. Wanting to feel me some of that taste such air, feel the air around me. Thinking how could I know the world without knowing seeing certain things first, how without that might I be able to find my own way. I remember Dear Deidre problem pages a daily habit some guy wrote in once after being worse for drink after writing the words I'M FUCKING BRILLIANT blue gloss the outside of the house. I remember a man in a chicken suit cycled through a supermarket in Skipton and terrorized the staff. I remember using toenails as toothpicks. I remember days when it all seemed too much, remember days too full spilling out from themselves. I remember things left un, only ever half never fucking said.

I remember Carol Vorderman, remember coming home with time enough to catch *Countdown*. He would be poised then, body shape still evident in his chair by the window as he waited with a cup of tea on the cusp of being poured. I remember it especially after Helen and Chris had left, coming home shirt untucked and ready for a sit-down but for him, the anticipation within him at company again. Whether it was my being better at the numbers round or because he had been stifling all day, but I remember him as always being ready, eager at least for a walk round the block. Worn thin, it would take more than just the suggestion to persuade me, and it seems that every day we did go I would have to be lured out by the promise of a quiz, a pound rewarded for five correct answers. Changing out of uniform and walking down the garden, the sequence of rocks that allowed us to cross the beck and into the Clough. Always in my mind the event takes place in winter, damp shortening days as dad did his best to read the woodland, on the lookout for subjects beyond trees out of leaf.

When I was in my early mid twenties and already then failing as a poet I stumbled across a phrase which somehow eclipsed the previous totality of my output. Never quite satisfied, it would not stay still, kept moving from poem to poem as the rest of my work struggled to match up. For me – and I think this all too clearly shows at least one of my failings as a poet – the phrase made a perfect, irrefutable sense in and of itself, required no further explanation after all I had done to uncover it. For me it contained it all. Perhaps it is this which was my weakness, that I expected too much from my reader, expected those nigh-on-hypothetical entities to readily discern, eke out the laminate meanings I had concealed in my burnt offerings. *The archaeology of posture*. A description of the bodily evidence within a chair just risen from, the particular quality of nothingness created by a body freshly gone. Depressions formed by the back and shoulders, the restless contouring of his arse. Arms abraded by the patter and scratch of fingernails in need of being cut.

Lingering presence of body shape within a favoured chair but not just that, not that only. The phrase — and I still think it might have been able to achieve this, might have been capable of achieving such a meaning if placed within a suitable and sufficient context — was intended to contain something of the archaeology or heritage from which posture might be formed, the manner in which posture might be said to belong within a certain hierarchy or structure of genetic inheritance. Grandpa Lancashire tapping his fingers while listening to the Test Match. Me here now, worrying my body into this chair. However many generations, failed poet upon failed poet sighing on the outbreath of our tiredness.

I would come home and he would be there, the archaeology of his posture all too apparent in the armchair just risen from. The system of reward and barter he would go through so as we might go out for a quiz. The identification of trees in winter. I remember the ash was an easy one, but after that I would struggle.

The kestrel is the only bird of prey that can actually hover.

How many's that today?

Six.

No it's, seven actually I, I saw another one, one none of you saw.

You didn't.

Michael stop lying.

I did I saw another one.

That's good Michael.

Seven already well, we're going somewhere aren't we but.
Not even past Birming.

Don't mention it.

Mention what?

The B-word.

The B-word?

Don't say it out loud.

Sorry love it's, the B-word, no. How could I forget. Not
even past the B-word and we've, seven kestrels already. We
should be well into double figures, might have hit twenty
even by the time we make the ferry.

Don't get ahead of yourself Sinclair.

It's not like I.

Even so.

Oh I shouldn't have thought it'd be all that bad love, not at
this time.

You never know do you though?

Not with the B-word no but, that's the beauty of it isn't it. The frisson.

The frisson?

The mystery of it yes. Something to keep us on our toes.

Well if you put it like that but, really Sinclair, I've had about enough time on my toes lately.

So you've been telling me.

Not this again Sinclair.

I haven't said a word.

I don't know it's, really now.

What?

Sinclair the road.

I'm concentrating love really, what do you take me for?

Not while you're lighting your cigarette you're not.

Well it's lit now isn't it love and, what's that you three, let's not have any squabbling in the back now.

It's Michael he's.

Just listen to what he's saying dad.

It is though, even if you don't believe me it is. They don't have to be as hot as you think, it's not about the heat, not only about the heat. You can get cold deserts and, Antarctica actually. Antarctica is the largest desert not the Sahara actually.

See dad?

Have you heard him?

It's always snowing Michael.

No he's, listen to your brother for once. I'm not sure if

it's the whole of Antarctica but it's within it certainly, the continental interior.

But it's always snowing.

How can it be a desert when it's covered in snow?

I think that maybe that's, that it might well be the wind, picking things up.

Really Sinclair?

Yes it's, I always wanted to go to Antarctica.

You always wanted to go everywhere Sinclair.

Why not love it's, what's stopping us.

The children are at school Sinclair.

There must be schools down there or we could homeschool them, away-school them if you like.

Not when Christopher's in the middle of his GCSEs we couldn't.

I'm sure it's something could be managed love.

And mess things up for life Sinclair really, what would we even do for work I do wonder sometimes, if you ever stop to think.

But thinking's what I do, what I'm always doing besides, there's always work isn't there, I'm sure the Survey could do with some hands we could, I don't know, we could always try our luck being research scientists couldn't we.

Neither of us is a scientist Sinclair.

How hard can it be, counting penguins all day?

They all look the same Sinclair.

Well that's as may be but, come on now love. Time waits for snowman.

Sinclair.

Love?

That's abysmal Sinclair.

Abominable you mean?

It's, honestly now. What did I even marry. I think that should be about the final word on the matter.

Something to be thinking about, isn't it though.

I don't know Sinclair sometimes with you it's like, what did I marry it's, I don't know, if you were a boat you'd be dreaming of a hill.

What's wrong with that it's, a boat can dream can't it we, we're doing alright, aren't we love?

We're getting there.

To think, we'll be in France tonight camping tonight and it won't be long, a week or two, within the fortnight we should be seeing vultures.

Oh, we will won't we?

Sitting with a coffee, a cerveza in Spain watching the vultures.

It'll be, won't it yes. Of an evening with the food cooking and a cup of wine.

Oh but, the wine though love. To be drinking out in the open air and knowing, the space of it all, knowing that if you don't want to do anything come the morning you don't have to. It doesn't matter. You don't have to do anything the morning after if you don't want. The taste of it then, drinking from a plastic cup and it just about getting dark, all that summer in the air.

At the end of the day sitting out.

The cricket's horn. No more than, what that might be.

To be sleeping under canvas and, the all of it though. Not having to worry about lights left on.

Oh, douce campagna it's, worth saying goodbye to English milk for.

Getting up with the day.

I know love, it's. Croissants all steaming hot.

Sinclair?

So very much cheese.

Sinclair.

The good stuff, it's.

Sinclair!

Yes love?

I think you'd better slow down Sinclair.

We're on the motorway love, I can't just be slowing down.

But, that rattle Sinclair that noise.

What noise love?

That rattle Sinclair really, you're getting as bad as your father can't you hear it?

I'm not sure I.

Sinclair it's getting louder I, I think we'd better pull over Sinclair.

Love really I can't, we can't just go pulling onto the hard shoulder you know.

Not the hard shoulder then the services, the next available services.

Service station!

Are we going to a service station are we?

Yes we'll be pulling in in shit, I can't remember what the last sign said.

There's no need to be getting historical love.

Hysterical Sinclair.

Still it's, we don't have to panic just yet.

Can we get travel sweets?

Travel sweets can we?

Yes I'll, we'll give you some money but, really Sinclair, honestly, I think you ought to slow down.

Love I'll have to put the hazards on if we go any slower.

Then put the hazards on Sinclair.

Really love, it'll be something and nothing.

Are we having another breakdown?

Please dad, not again.

No nobody's, it's just, your mother's just fussing for a change is all.

Are we going to make it?

Enough of this you lot, doubting me again it's, will be something worked free in the back if it's anything.

We won't have to sleep by a roundabout will we?

Really Helen, there's no need to panic.

Is it the chassis?

No Michael, it is not the chassis no.

PART THREE

The sea would have been out when it came back to me. Of that much I am sure. I had been living and working at the cove on the coast for long enough that it had begun to feel slightly weary, something of a chore, the initial romance of falling asleep to wavesong spread thin, misplaced somewhere within the general dissatisfactions of shift work. Walking the beach, I had taken to reminding (attempting to remind) myself how it had felt when I first arrived, how lucky I had then considered myself, able to stumble out the door and into the bay, my dreams of beachcombing a reality now. I was lucky and I remained one of the lucky ones, able to step out onto the rocks whenever tide and rota obliged.

It was my primary outlet at the time, the manner in which my creative impulses were, if not satisfied, then at least somewhat placated. What Paul Klee said about drawing being the act of taking a line for a walk, so it was for me then. Not that I considered myself my own paintbrush, had dipped my feet in ink: I was not walking so as to later transcribe it, to attempt to transpose the language of walking into words, to turn my footsteps into something other and better, but simply to walk, consider walking itself an act of creation.

If the tide was rising I was restricted to the sands where Stoupe Beck meets the sea, watching gannets nosedive throughout the bay. When it was in I might head along the coastal path towards Whitby before looping down the cinder track. But on that day my walking was influenced by a split shift rather than the North Sea. This opened things out again, the line taken up to me. Whether to traipse over pebbles or sand, risk wet feet by venturing too close to rock pools or the bladderwrack where turnstones scurried in what I think is best described as a quixotic fashion, beaks tilting at windmills.

There are of course people who do not think that thought, thinking itself can prove to be an aesthetic pursuit (matter of principle), have not been instructed from an early age that it is only ideas won through walking that contain any worth. What might they have made of me, where I had got to, walking the bay with my childhood, education, my anxiety dreams and ambition to one day finish reading Proust, wondering to myself why it was me who walked the bay, had even come to that place, what it was that had brought me there. I had failed as a poet, was getting myself to a place where I might again be able to fail as a poet. I told myself that I was a lucky one, more than fortunate to be experiencing this, the audible puttering of cliffs as they crumbled to the beach, lumps of clay rolled by the tide into monstrous eggs. More than lucky to be stepping again into all of this.

I told myself not to think of those internet-shared photos, people I had known at school celebrating anniversaries with cocktails in the sunshine, on Caribbean holidays, all dressed up on their work trips overseas. That was not what I had wanted.

I had never wanted that. I said to myself what I had taken to saying to myself, that I should be thinking on a global scale. That with running water and sanitation, the roof for now over my head and this leisure time, I was one of the luckiest ones. It sometimes helped.

That morning (and if it was not that morning then it was a morning quite like it, a morning that might well have been that morning), between the serving of the breakfast and the beginning of the housekeeping, I had been up to it in bin juice. A girl about twelve, maybe thirteen, had removed her retaining brace so as to eat, wrapped it in blue paper towel and placed it on the table. Scrunched up, the blue paper towel looked like blue paper towel scrunched up. Someone in her party had thrown it in with the rubbish. We changed the bags after each service and I had gone to the compound, taken out the likely candidates and brought them to the girl and her family. I had removed my kitchen whites and gone elbow-deep in the mushiness, teabags and egg yolk, albumen, scraps of toast gone soggy with it all, bacon fat and apple cores and those sausages we got complaints about, the brainbits in them. They did say that no two days would be the same. That you would not get that working in an office.

Things, and the weight they contain. How gravity accelerates beyond reason and mass.

Amongst that dwindling miscellany, the shales and the mudstones that made up the cliffs of the bay, there was a particular substance the colour of Blaenau Ffestiniog slate. It would fragment and sheer off in angular chunks, lumps tottering from the main body of the cliffs on what seemed a daily basis. When freshly exposed the scarring seemed all but alive, a bleeding, angered rust. A gem collector who would often stay at the cove told me it was not the rock but the mineral deposits within it that caused such a reaction, exposed iron ore screaming into the air. The emotions would soon fade, tones dulling and soothed so that it was not possible to distinguish the sections of the cliff that had fallen away in the past fortnight from those of a month, six weeks ago. Seeing it as I did that day (colours breathing, spitting raw and active) served as some sort of reminder, not just of where I was, but what it actually meant to be there. Blink and you miss it, disorder always on the increase. We should not need this, should not need to view evidence of rockfall to appreciate where it is we walk, should not need to witness collapse to keep ourselves in check. But sometimes we do.

The seals beneath Peak were in unusual voice that day (and again, if it was not that day then it was a day much like it, a day towards the end of my final season living and working at the cove on the coast), sprawled out across the scaurs and sort of half-howling half-singing together, perhaps thirty seals making what might best be described as a plaintive or plangent sound, a part-drowned choir struggling to keep heads above water. I thought about recording them, about someone recording them, that wailing unison the first motif towards some grand arrangement or symphony, mammals working towards a common end. If only it could be so easy.

The tide was out far enough for me to linger down there and I did some of that, aware that it might be my ultimate visit that year (I have not yet been back) and again reminding (attempting to remind) myself what it had been like to first come out this way, to walk beneath the headland and feel as if everything out there was my personal discovery. Something I had read about geology had formed a series of rounded platforms, politely elevated and known locally as the Mermaids' Dining Tables. How privileged I had felt when first I found them, learnt their names. They had reminded me of rock formations on the New Zealand coastline, photo opportunities for the kind of person I might once have been, a gap year student expecting life to fall conveniently at his feet. To uncover such things for one's self, seemingly untouched on the Yorkshire coast. Yes, it had been a privilege, a stroke of fortune to find myself out that way. I *was* lucky, thankful for those mistakes and failures which had brought me here, in this space between shifts. Some place to be between the cleaning of the toilets and short-order cooking.

The beginning of the path up to Peak was in a worse state than when I had last been out so far, particulate earth no match for all that moonlust, incessant longings of the sea. I wondered what it might be like were I to come back, after further winters, further winters' storms. The seals maintained their harmonies. I looked over the sweep of the bay, ribs of rock protruding out into the water as brown-dappled gulls drifted overhead. I wondered what I might miss about it, how I would feel when I had caught up on sleep, shift patterns faded from my body. Out to sea there was one of those phantom bits of rainbow you sometimes get out to sea. Not long and I would be on my way.

In my mind I always seem to find that yellowhammers are

singing, declining cheese with their bread in amongst gorse bushes and bramble, though I cannot imagine that actually to have been the case that day. The gorse was not in flower, did not smell of coconut. It must surely have been too late in the year for such a carry-on. But there we were. Late as it was, I thought why not when it came to visiting the tea rooms up there, cut across the golf course to the village on the clifftop. Minimum wage had constrained me, and I had taken to taking a flask out, those unruined quids going some way to securing my bus fare home. But what is life if not to occasionally live it up? I ordered a coffee which arrived on a tray, the proprietor calling me *sir* in spite of the mud on my trousers (earthquake in my eyes) as he brought the cafetière and milk jug and bowl of irregular sugar cubes, the cup and the saucer and the teaspoon.

It was the teaspoon that did for me. The teaspoon that opened me up.

When called as children to the table we would run and squabble in our family resemblance, elbows out as we fought over who got to use a certain type of cutlery, for reasons obscure called the Hot Set. Holding them in your hands was victory enough. No league tables were ever collated, no question as to who might be on a consistent run of form going into the next meal. From this distance (the lifetimes in me separate) it is a struggle to understand what it was that kept our interest going. For certain the Hot Set did stand out, distinguished itself from the rest of the cutlery in the drawer, but still I wonder what beyond the name Helen and Chris had given it put it so far in front. Without such a reference the game could not have been, but maybe there is something lacking from my study of formal logic which means I cannot pull one from the other. If A = B and B = C, then maybe it is not so great a leap to think that A must also = C. If the cutlery = the Hot Set and the Hot Set = the game, then it must be the case that the cutlery = the game. If I played a game with my siblings then maybe my siblings were the game. Who is to know, might say why certain things cohere. Earlier that year I had asked a group of civil servants if they had gone into the profession because of a love for the nineteenth-century Russian novel. Who is to know what lifts things from out of themselves.

From the Hot Set but not *of* the Hot Set. Placed within the grand, unifying principles of the Hot Set but not belonging to, no part its one-offness, the unique and particular Hot Set we squabbled over as kids, the teaspoon was never part of our concern. There in my hands it could not have belonged anywhere else. Of Korean production, its handle had been embossed with a soft explosion of cuboid forms, a scaled-down version of our dessert spoon, elegant as the first snowdrop of the year. For something like that to bring so much back, to unravel me. I remembered Helen and Chris, the three of us rumbling our way to the kitchen, scratching and clawing for a little taste of glory. I remembered catapults, broken glass. Spools of cassette tape discarded on the pavement. Pornography in the shrubbery, cocks and balls scrawled in exercise books. A man in Skipton who cycled round a supermarket and threatened staff. I thought about what it was like when there was no one left to play with, talk to, those long months after Helen had gone to university when I would stand each day in her room, weighing up the emptiness around me. Those years before I myself left home. I thought about my brother and my sister now, their children learning to read and write as I, on my split shift, dilated on a spoon. I remembered that other game, the one with a central post, the game where you would run and hide, try and make it back to the post without being noticed, the final person uttering a sacred word or phrase, some magic number to set the captured free. I remembered wild garlic, the smell of wild garlic at the bottom of the garden, crossing the beck at the bottom of the garden to step into the Clough. In the spoon. It was all in that spoon. There. The bowl of the spoon contained all those mealtimes, the three of us fighting over cutlery, overdone carrots and the gristle on pork chops, mealtimes and what came after mealtimes, homework to be done, mum with her marking in front of the telly as dad quoted his own poetry, did not consider himself unwell.

I saw him there, saw my father in the bowl, the concavity of that spoon, saw the two of us out for a walk and calling in for a pint, some drink or two together – a rare occasion when it was me who had bought the round. For as long as I could remember it had only ever taken a mouthful, his first initial sip for the bitter to lose its head, no residue lingering like spiderweb on the glass. He would blame his medication, the chemical synthesis of his saliva imbalanced by that ongoing rattle of drugs. When I had asked for a taste something intangible was missing or tarnished, notes too subtle to even be flavours. I saw things I'd had to do. Places I'd had to go. In the spoon in the tea rooms I saw myself in Seahouses, saw myself in the queue for the tourist boat and stood within the tourist boat as it made its way out from Seahouses and on to the Farnes without a hat, in that spoon in the tea rooms I saw that I was without a hat as I handed over my money and boarded the boat, controlled my dread by looking at the horizon, disembarked on Inner Farne in breeding season, the seabirds there, the terns. I saw Arctic terns a turbulence above me, a cloud like bees above me shrieking tirrick tern Arctic tern, the squabble and squawk of them Arctic tern tirrick tern, tirrick tirrick Arctic tern Arctic tirrick tirrick tern, dive-bombing Arctic tern tirrick tern as I went too close, stepped away, again went too close to the nests. I saw myself a captive there, incapable of movement as the Arctic terns in their racket swelled above me tirrick tern Arctic tern, the cloud above me Arctic tern tirrick tern, churning and shrieking Arctic tern tirrick tern tirrick tirrick Arctic tern as if that colony possessed then but one voice, as if it were a single body or entity above me swirling, one vast white bird unknown to the police and arguing amongst itself as I stood without a hat, unprotected, blood trickling from a peck to the head. I tasted blood. I tasted blood trickling down my forehead and over my glasses. My vision gone red as still I did not move away from the nests, the colony, the cloud squawking in agitated morass as still I did not move until the hand on my arm, voice in my ear, the hand leading me away from the nests and back towards the boat. The ranger who shared her tea with me, talked me down. In the bowl of it. The spoon contained it all.

Sometimes I allow myself to wonder just what it took to return from those places, again get back to where I might be allowed (allow myself) to fail as a poet and fail as a man, fail those small and daily, necessary failures of someone who might be considered well and active, an able participant in the world. Time/sleep/orange juice. I do wonder sometimes if it was any more than time and sleep and orange juice. Understanding. In an attempt once to make something of it, to turn that episode into fiction or create a fiction from out of the episode and its aftermath, I wrote about a father and a son working together in a river, the bend of a river which cut or threatened to cut into their land. *It was another worry to graft through. Jostled numb, the boy had a look of grief about his face, as if something within it were gone forever. As if a fire or a spark had gone missing from his eyes, in overexcitement burnt too far. As if something vital had been taken from him. Something he himself had given away, allowed to be taken. The old man attempted to breathe things alive once more, get the flames back going. Pinning hope on the process: dislodging rocks from the river together, lifting with the knees not the back to mound them into a defence. What lengths he went to retrieve him, get the boy home. The harsh words spoken. The insistence. Guiding his son over hot coals, wading through mired sands, shifting as all the while he mopped night sweats from the boy's brow, saying hush, hush, there's no need to talk, you don't have to, hush. Quiet, my son, don't speak. How not to force the issue. How the issue had had to be forced.*

What do we even learn, given time? That with a touch of practice, some little bit of shuffling, you can get away with cooking pizza and garlic bread at the same temperature.

Sometimes it will feel as if we have done the least, but at the very least we have been positive when it comes to the making of our mistakes. That our errors are all the learning we might ever hope for. There is more than one way to cook rice. It is sometimes better to go easy on the salt. What do we even, ever learn? That even those troubles that seem for their while to engulf the world, eclipse it even, even they will reduce, be contained within the world again, through time and time and time again fading, like spent echoes in a barrel.

With the spoon in my hand I did my best not to shake as I drank my coffee and looked at the clock. I thought about pocketing it, thought better of myself. Outside, the breeze was picking up. A bar or two of reception flickered on my phone. Over buffeted years I had developed a method for such conditions. By sheltering my head within a windproof jacket it was just about possible to maintain a conversation. I tried Helen. Twice in a row her phone rang through to answering machine. Third time round I left a message, did my best to explain what had occurred. Hot Set, I said. I am calling about the Hot Set.

ACKNOWLEDGEMENTS

This book has taken a lot of doing. Too many people have helped me in too many ways to adequately mention here, but I would especially like to thank –

My parents.

Neil Griffiths, Damian Lanigan and Lamorna Ash.

Sarah Terry.

James Tookey.

Maria de Souza at Off the Shelf Festival of Words.

Alex Blenkinsop, Claire-Jane Carter, Paul Collins, Lucia Fiordelmondo, Sarah Jane Knight-Markiegi, Ian Nesbitt, Ben Owen-Smith, Alastair Smith, Stefan Tobler, Jon Trew, Helen Wynne-Kean.

Ric Booth.

Ryan Pasquill.

THE WAY THE DAY BREAKS

DAVID ROBERTS

First published in 2023
by Weatherglass Books

001

Cover design by Luke Bird
Text design and typesetting by James Tookey
Printed in the U.K. by TJ Books, Padstow

A CIP record for this book is published by the British Library

ISBN: 978-1-7399833-9-0

www.weatherglassbooks.com

Weatherglass
Books